3. -
3.12

Feb. 21, 1959

1114 Laguna St.
Santa Barbara, Calif.

The Legacy of Doctor Wiley

Courtesy of Assn. of Food and Drug Officials of the U.S.

DR. HARVEY W. WILEY
1844 - 1930

The Legacy

of

Doctor Wiley

By

MAURICE NATENBERG

Regent House • Chicago

Library of Congress Catalog Card Number 57-8422

PRINTED IN THE UNITED STATES OF AMERICA

$\mathcal{J}$NTRODUCTION

T HE AUTHOR of this book has done a great service in recalling to younger generations the life and work of Harvey W. Wiley, M.D. We are hereby reminded that the Pure Food Law, enacted at Dr. Wiley's behest, is adequate for the protection of our health only if properly administered. Enforcement, however, has never been effective because of apathy of the American people and aggressiveness of a few individuals and organizations with predatory interests in its evasion.

The rate of industrialization of our society has had even more to do with failure to enforce the provisions of the law Dr. Wiley fathered. The 125 years since the Industrial Revolution began in America have not been sufficient for us to adapt ourselves, as a people, to the machine and its technology. While increasing our standard of living, problems of an urban culture have resulted. Not the least of these are economic pressure on the 6 per cent of our people who now grow food for the rest of us and our demands for processed and packaged foods for convenient storage. 125 years ago, food production required the work of 96 per cent of the population and food was largely consumed in season and near its source. The growth of cities created a need for foods from faraway places, leading to a demand for fruits and vegetables out of season. Necessities of shipping and distribution made preservation and storage major problems. Technology met these problems with a host of devitalizing methods and hundreds of chemicals to preserve or to improve appearance. The American diet lost much of its health-giving qualities with refinement of wheat flour, sugar, and salt. It was further vitiated by addition of bleaches, coloring matter, and chemical preservatives. Chronic degenerative diseases arising

5

from the accumulative effects of all this pseudoscience were obscured in our vital statistics by victories of medicine over infectious diseases.

But what is this all about? Aren't we the healthiest people who ever lived? Haven't we doubled our life expectancy within the lifetime of men now living?

Technology has contributed to better health by designing healthier dwellings, providing pure drinking water, destroying breeding places of mosquitoes and other disease-bearing insects, and helping to produce foodstuffs at an ever-increasing rate while protecting them against spoilage.

This book is concerned with the other side of the record—the indiscriminate use of nearly 800 chemicals in our foods. In the case of over half of these no one knows whether or not they are harmful in an accumulative way.

To understand these poisons, we must gain a new and more accurate concept of life's process and its relation to maximum health. Each of us has a body composed of billions of tiny units called cells. Each of these is a living separate unit joined with other cells to make a human being. Through evolutionary processes these cells have given up their co-operative state to become specialists in communication, transportation, food supply, locomotion, and defense. To carry on the life process, each of these cells must digest food, excrete its wastes, and repair itself.

Every reaction depends upon a chemical response triggered and controlled by a specific enzyme system. It is the function of the protein of the cell to join with a particular vitamin and one of the mineral nutrients, originally from the soil, to form an enzyme with a highly specialized function. Each cell must contain from 50,000 to 100,000 of these enzyme systems ready always to go to work in a millionth of a second. Some have been assigned the task of remembering when you had mumps or measles or diphtheria and being prepared to defend against these specific germs for the rest of your life.

What most of us fail to appreciate is that each group of the enzyme systems is affected by the merest trace of certain chemicals —often as little as one part in a million, or less. Not until properly planned experiments—using several generations of the most susceptible animals—have been carried out with negative results, can anyone say that the accumulative effects are not harmful. Fluorida-tion of the public water supply is a notable example of a poison administered as a compulsory medication without much information. Dr. Wiley always insisted upon the sound policy that it should be up to the proponent of a new chemical to prove it is not harmful.

The specific mineral and vitamin as well as the building stones for the proteins must be in the cell at the same time and in proper proportions if the enzyme system is to be in perfect working order. Then each cell is doing its assigned task with a minimum of wear and tear. Under such ideal circumstances all mammals, including man, would live about five times as long as they take to mature. With man, life expectancy would be from 90 to 125 years, com-pared with the present 68 years.

We of this country were using, five years ago, enough pesticides to kill more than 15 million persons annually. Since then, their usage has increased and more deadly ones developed. Before 1945 we regularly produced crop surpluses without the use of such poisons. But now the experts in bug poisoning have convinced us that without these chemicals we cannot raise enough to eat, that millions will get sick and die from insect-borne diseases, our flower gardens will become unsightly, our mattresses alive with bedbugs, and our clothes full of holes. Such is not the case in a country which has proved it can eradicate insect-borne diseases without the use of these poisons and which developed synthetic fibers no insect will eat!

It should be clear by now that this book is most timely. Our citizens must come to realize that whenever something is added to or taken away from a natural food that the product is inferior. It should be evident, too, that the Food and Drug Administration must have the manpower, the finances, and full public support to effect enforcement of the principles set forth by that great servant of mankind, Harvey W. Wiley, M.D.

I would beseech everyone to read this book, to urge others to do likewise, and to remember, "No king ever wielded a scepter more powerful than a 5-cent pencil in the hands of a citizen when he sits down to write his representatives in Congress."

JONATHAN FORMAN, M.D.

Dublin, Ohio
March 1957

So am I impelled to leave a

legacy to all right-minded people,

namely,

to re-establish the work of my hands

in the days which are to come.

HARVEY W. WILEY
An Autobiography

ACKNOWLEDGMENTS

With deep appreciation we offer our thanks to the following firms and organizations who either directly or indirectly have helped in the preparation of this work:

The Association of Food and Drug Officials of the United States; Abbott Laboratories; National Live Stock Meat Board; The Bobbs-Merrill Company; The Blakiston Company; Hanover College; Purdue University; The Lee Foundation for Nutritional Research and to Mrs. Bernice Barnes for her invaluable editorial services and suggestions.

$\mathcal{F}$OREWORD

JUNE 30, 1956, marked the fiftieth anniversary of the Pure Food and Drug Act. The milestone was commemorated by many tributes to Dr. Harvey W. Wiley, father of the law, who crusaded for it so long and so valiantly. The canning, packing, chemical, and pharmaceutical industries, Food and Drug Administration officials, and many others—who in some manner benefited from the law—joined in homage to Dr. Wiley's life and work. The Post Office Department issued a special commemorative stamp. All avenues of expression were utilized in publicizing the occasion.

This book is a further effort to respect and honor Dr. Wiley's many contributions to the public welfare as scientist, educator, and government official. The highest respect we could pay to his memory would be to practice the principles of nutrition he advocated. His nutritional concepts and food standards constitute a legacy to the world which he believed would lead to better health and increased happiness and longevity. If the reader is inspired to follow Dr. Wiley's teachings, it could be the finest of all tributes.

MAURICE NATENBERG

Chicago, Illinois
March 1957

$\mathcal{I}$LLUSTRATIONS

11

CONTENTS

Page

DR. WILEY AT HIS DESK

CHAPTER I

Formative Years

AS A MAN, a scientist and a government official, Harvey W. Wiley reflected the splendid influences of his birth, his era and his environment. The man who fought so indefatigably for beneficial and wholesome foods and was ever opposed to fraud and chicanery acted in accord with the highest ethical principles instilled in him from the day of his birth; he could not act otherwise.

Harvey Wiley's forebears were American pioneers who had fought in the Revolutionary War. He was the third boy and sixth child born to Lucinda Weir Maxwell Wiley and Preston Pritchard Wiley. His birthplace was in a traditional log cabin on October 18, 1844 in the vicinity of Kent, Indiana. It was a beautiful region; the land was still virgin and many of the hardwood trees later so lamentably despoiled to clear the land for ground, were still standing. Years later Dr. Wiley regretfully told of his own part in destroying the black walnut trees on the family farm.

There were about 125 arable acres on their land which provided almost all of the Wileys' needs. They raised their own food and sold the surplus. The wood stand provided fuel and lumber as well as maple sugar and fruit. A herd of sheep supplied wool which Mrs. Wiley spun and sewed for their clothing. Southern Indiana was a wonderful place for an active, healthy boy to live. Fish and game were still plentiful in the woods which Indians had still roved not many years before.

It was an age when only the skilled, industrious and resourceful

13

could survive and procure the necessities which today are so easily bought. The average farmer was not just a tiller of the soil but a woodsman, a herdsman, a carpenter and a craftsman. He built his own home and furniture and even forged his own tools. All his riches were but the product of his own dexterity and craftsmanship.

Man was close to nature; the peace and solitude of the woods were just a few yards distant. On his table were only fresh and natural foods. His air was pure and fragrant, unpolluted by fumes, dust or smoke; his water, whether from stream, spring or well, was pure and invigorating. These were the simple yet priceless riches Harvey Wiley enjoyed in his youth and which he devoted his entire career to bringing in some measure to the American public.

He was also blessed with learned and highly devout parents. Besides farming, Harvey's father was also skilled at plastering, at times served very capably as a schoolteacher, and also taught Sunday School for over sixty years. He was a principled man, public spirited and neighborly and if somewhat austere and stern was nevertheless fair and just. Harvey Wiley characterized his father as an "Aurelius" whose punishment for childhood transgressions was swift and certain, though never too harsh.

Harvey learned to read and write spontaneously, practically by instinct so to speak and without formal instruction of any kind. When he was about four, his father was teaching and brought him each morning to class, placing him in a chalk-drawn circle from which he was forbidden to stray. As he sat in his enclosure, listening to his father teach and demonstrate, the instruction took root in his fertile brain. One day as his father was explaining a problem in addition, Harvey suddenly called out:

"Father, I can do that sum."

To the amazement of all, he made good his boast.

From his father Harvey inherited a deep love of learning; respect and obedience came naturally to him. He would no more dream of disobeying his parents than running away from home. Early he learned to share the family work; first assisting his mother at her spinning wheel; later his father about the farm. Harvey was cautioned against being quarrelsome and belligerent but to be quick to defend himself from attack. These teachings stood him in good stead in the years when he became embroiled with powerful interests. Though never flinching from battle, he also never sought a quarrel.

In that day, an education was very hard to secure. It was consequently highly treasured. Teachers were few and poorly paid. Only those with genuine zeal taught, and they taught well. In spite of the short and infrequent school terms, the meager facilities and scarcity of books, children learned and learned thoroughly.

His teachers made an indelible impression on Harvey Wiley's mind for though his autobiography was written at the age of eighty-five, he recalled their names and personalities with fondness and the excellence of their instruction with gratitude. He dwelt in particular on a Reverend Brazelton, who taught with infinite patience and skill and commanded the highest respect without the threats, scoldings or corporal punishment considered necessary in those days.

Not only the instruction of his teachers, but the lessons of nature learned in wresting a living from the soil, were to become invaluable in Harvey Wiley's future work. His career eventually became an extension of his first work on the farm. He learned to milk, to plow, the art of dropping corn seeds to grow in lines straight and tall and to harvest grain either with the old-fashioned cradle or sickle. Threshing was usually done on a co-operative basis by sharing the few machines known as "ground hogs" among the various farmers. While awaiting the machine, the grain for the family use was threshed and separated by riding the horses over it on the floor of the barn. After cleaning, the grain was taken to the mill.

So also was the corn milled and it was on such simple nourishing food that the Wiley children were raised. Their standard evening meal in the winter was hot mush with skim milk; for breakfast it was fried mush. Their maple trees supplied sugar. When the trees disappeared, sorghum cane was cultivated and it gave them sugar for a long time.

It was Harvey himself who planted the first sorghum used on their farm, and it was also the first planted in that region. The seed had been imported to Indiana from Asia in 1857 and supplied to Mr. Wiley by their Congressman. Harvey's first taste of the delicious sweetness of sorghum convinced him of its excellence. When molasses became unprocurable during the Civil War the sorghum provided a worthy replacement. This then was a fore-runner of the influences which were to make Harvey Wiley the "father of the beet sugar industry."

Money was scarce those days. As a lad of ten or so, Harvey's skill in dropping corn seeds became celebrated. A neighbor hired him for a day's planting. When at the end of his fourteen-hour stint, Harvey was paid a silver quarter, he became so excited he refused supper and ran all the way home to show it to his parents. In later life, he prized that quarter as highly as any honor or distinction of his career.

At sixteen, Harvey Wiley tried to enlist in the war between the States. Though his strapping size made him look like the required eighteen years, he was too truthful to falsify his age and had to be content with joining the Indiana State Militia—which accepted boys of sixteen.

On attaining his eighteenth year, Harvey had had only five terms of schooling, though they were excellently augmented by his father's instruction. In 1863, because his schoolteacher's professed Southern sympathies outraged his sense of patriotism, Harvey felt unable to attend his classes and decided to enroll at Hanover College only five miles from the farm.

With his father's consent, Harvey walked to the college and timidly enrolled. He arranged for his lodging at two dollars per week and to bring food from his home. Each Saturday at daybreak he walked to the farm, had his breakfast and then worked. Each Sunday he carried back his provisions for the coming week.

The diet of the future crusader for pure foods was simple and rarely contained meat. Harvey and his younger brother who later joined him at Hanover, for the most part ate potatoes, cornmeal and sorghum molasses. Butter came from their farm and they arranged to have their flour baked into bread. Some of their whole wheat, unbolted and undegerminated flour, they prepared as mush. On this simple but adequate diet, Harvey Wiley and his brother subsisted all during their college years.

He wrote of those years with keen appreciation for the excellence of the instruction at Hanover and the zeal and devotion of his teachers, so meagerly rewarded in a monetary way yet wholly oblivious to their poverty in their love of knowledge. Far from decrying the poverty of Hanover, Dr. Wiley saw in it only a powerful incentive to learning. In his autobiography he wrote:

> There is a certain danger in overcapitalization of an institution of learning. Poverty has its uses in academic instruction as well as in the building of character. The teachers who have to struggle for existence, in my opinion, have a decided advantage over those who are pampered by large incomes, easy chairs and luxury which tends to deaden the finer instincts of the pedagogic profession. One reason for the great success of the small college I feel to be due to the financial struggle which it usually has to undergo. Hanover was a rich beneficiary of poverty. I carried away a fine heritage from personal contact with teachers and students. This I regard as of greater value to me in after life than the fact that I was able to stand at the head of my class from beginning to the end of my college career.

Courtesy of Hanover College

Except for minor changes, this was Hanover College during Harvey Wiley's student days.

The great reverence Harvey Wiley retained for his father's principles is exemplified in this anecdote of college days. He was approached by a fellow student who later became an affluent newspaper owner and banker, and asked to join in organizing a Greek-letter fraternity. With the gentlest of refusals, he declined on the grounds his father was opposed to secret organizations.

College days were interrupted by an enlistment for a one-hundred-day service in the war when Harvey reached eighteen. On his only military expedition, he was taken seriously ill and sent home. His invalidism lingered for almost an entire year. Recovery came just after the war ended and Lincoln was assassinated.

Shyness and timidity handicapped Harvey Wiley as a student. Even as a child, he dreaded to recite in class and only after years of diligent effort was he able to overcome this weakness. At Hanover he compelled himself to join a literary society which required each member to speak before the group.

To prevent embarrassing slips, Harvey first carefully prepared his talks in writing, then committed them to memory. It was an excellent discipline for the future which would call on him to address many distinguished audiences and to testify in Congressional hearings. This practice in reducing ideas to simple, understandable terms to be expressed orally no doubt accounts for the excellency of Dr. Wiley's writings which so lucidly clarified the most complex chemical problems.

It was perhaps significant that his first essay, read before the Philalethean Society of Hanover College, was on health.

CHAPTER II

Pregovernment Career

A FTER GRADUATING, Harvey Wiley taught school for a year in Lake County, Indiana. We can envision the tall, earnest yet somewhat shy young man teaching after the inspiring example set by his father, Reverend Brazelton, Dr. Scott, and other excellent instructors. He considered his monthly salary of sixty dollars as munificent as the twenty-five cents he earned as a boy for fourteen hours of planting corn. Harvey saved one hundred dollars during the six-month school term, which ended in the summer of 1868.

It was an appropriate time for this stalwart, serious young fellow of twenty-three to decide on a career. He chose medicine and as was customary in that day, first served an apprenticeship with a former Civil War comrade, Dr. E. S. Hampton of Milton, Kentucky, just across the Ohio River from Kent. The apprenticeship consisted of reading each day from Dr. Hampton's medical books, submitting to a quiz on what he read and also accompanying the doctor on his rounds. It was a practical and effective method of instruction, combining the theoretical with the practical, the objective with the abstract, and somewhat typical of Dr. Wiley's entire career. His work on the farm in raising food was no doubt invaluable for learning the chemistry of foods.

Like the farmer, the country doctor in those days was often a man of great ingenuity, resourcefulness and presence of mind. He did not have today's elaborate armamentarium of drugs, diagnostic helps, a vast literature, a great variety of surgical instruments, or the conveniences of hospitals and consultations with colleagues. Operations were often done in the kitchen with relatives serving as surgical assistants. Fortunately the people of that day were a hardy and robust lot with remarkable recuperative powers which survived the doctor's crude techniques.

One day they were called to attend a man shot in a brawl. He was sitting on a fence, nonchalantly whittling as he awaited their arrival. Dr. Hampton's examination disclosed a serious wound. The bullet had entered just above the navel, penetrating his body and emerging at a point along the spine. They cleaned and dressed the wound, though certain that internal injuries would be fatal. Yet a week or so later, completely healed, the patient rode on horseback to Dr. Hampton's office to ask for his bill.

Following his medical apprenticeship of one summer Harvey Wiley was offered the post of instructor of Latin and Greek at Northwestern Christian University, an institution of the Church of Disciples, now Butler University of Indianapolis. He accepted eagerly as it permitted arranging teaching there between his own classes at the Medical College of Indiana University. After three years spent in this pleasant and convenient arrangement, in 1871 Harvey Wiley the teacher became Harvey Wiley, M.D.

Misgivings of his competence, however, prevented him from embarking into practice. Instead, he taught science at the Central High School and shortly afterwards was elected to the chair of chemistry at the Medical College. Dr. Wiley also felt unprepared to engage in teaching chemistry without further study, and accepted with the provision that he be granted time for further preparation.

Dr. Wiley's misgivings arose after attending meetings of the American Association for the Advancement of Science held in Indianapolis in the summer of 1871. The insight he gained into genuine scientific procedures made him feel neither chemistry nor medicine had true scientific foundations. Later he wrote autobiographically:

> Let me use the matter of diet as illustration. No one had ever said anything to me from a scientific point of view about diet. In fact, little was known of dietary principles as we understand them today. All the practicing physician knew about diet he had learned from his clinical experience; and everyone knows what an unsafe guide is

clinical experience alone. The actual treatment of disease was chaotic. This and that remedy were tried without much knowledge of pharmacology or the ulterior effect of drugs.

Impressed by the principles of the Association for the Advancement of Science and by the membership of so many eminent professors from Harvard University, Dr. Wiley was attracted to that school for further scientific training. Among his many fine teachers were Dr. J. P. Cooke head of the department of chemistry, his assistants Charles Loring Jackson and Harry Hill and Professors Monroe and Tyndall.

Dr. Wiley was especially impressed by the great naturalist, Louis Agassiz whose lectures he reported for the *Indianapolis Journal*. That too, was ideal training for his future career. As the Chief of the Bureau of Chemistry his preparation was thorough and his education the best available in the United States, if not in all the world. The year of postgraduate study was terminated with a grueling examination, both oral and written, lasting seventeen days, after which he was awarded the degree of Bachelor of Science, *cum laude*. It was a proud moment when Harvey Wiley received his diploma from Charles W. Eliot, the "boy" president of Harvard.

Upon his return to Indianapolis, several posts were offered to him. He accepted that of chemistry head at Northwestern Christian University, teaching there mornings and from four to ten in the evening at the Medical College. This left the hours from noon to four free but even this idle time was not long open, for the high school called upon him to teach physiology during the illness of an instructor.

The consequences were inevitable. Overworked, eating irregularly and driving even his stalwart physique far beyond its powers, Dr. Wiley staggered to his house which his parents had fortunately come to share with him. Almost paralyzed, his case was diagnosed as cerebrospinal meningitis. The illness was severe—almost fatal. A leg amputation was considered imperative but his physicians did not operate, respecting what they believed was a dying wish. Recovery was slow and it was a year before this overzealous young man of thirty could walk without a cane.

Toward the end of that summer, Dr. Wiley was engaged as head of the chemistry department of Purdue University, scheduled to open its doors in 1874. In the fall, he reported for duty, taking with him a student in his junior year, John B. Harper, who became the first and only graduate of Purdue in the year 1875.

In 1878 Dr. Wiley obtained a year's leave of absence for study in Europe. This was indeed a tremendously fruitful year as it augmented an already splendid training. He attended clinics and seminars at the University of Vienna, meeting the renowned Dr. Billroth, one of the founders of modern surgery. At the General Hospital, affiliated with the University, he observed their treatment of typhoid fever, then common because of the polluted water supply.

Though he had not abandoned his plan to practice medicine already put off for some five years, Dr. Wiley felt no further inclination to study medicine. Instead, he proceeded to Berlin to attend classes with Professor Hoffman, the renowned chemist and master of experimental demonstrations. He also heard Helmholtz and Virchow, famous in physics and pathology. He was introduced to the polariscope by Dr. Sell, chemist of the Imperial Health Department. The polariscope was to become a valuable instrument for investigating sugars in the Bureau of Chemistry.

Bonn, Heidelberg and Leipzig were other stops on the Wiley itinerary of laboratory inspections. At Heidelberg he met and spoke to the great Robert Bunsen. From Europe, he carried back a passion for examining food products and a decision to abandon medicine for the study of food adulteration.

He returned to his teaching with renewed enthusiasm. Gradually, as his autobiography relates, fear of lecturing dissolved into enjoyment of it, as he acquired the knack of speaking extemporaneously without a manuscript and often without notes. The art of thinking on his feet arrived from speaking extemporaneously and avoiding a rigid outline.

Soon after returning from Europe, Dr. Wiley received an order from the Indiana State Board of Health to investigate the adulteration of honey, sirups and molasses with glucose. His extensive report was the first ever made on the subject in Indiana and also his first official paper on food adulteration. It later led to an embroilment with a food interest, on this occasion a comparatively minor one, the beekeepers. A colleague teaching chemistry in

Boston had sent a sample of artificial honey made with an artificial comb filled with glucose and capped with paraffin—the prototype of the comb which is now in general use.

After mentioning this comb somewhat humorously in an article for *Popular Science,* the beekeepers rose in wrath to call the allegation of its use as the "Wiley lie." For some years they continued the bitter attack, until Dr. Wiley finally came across the very machine used to manufacture the artificial combs. Armed with this evidence, he refuted their charges of falsification and warned of the great harm the honey industry would inflict upon itself by storing glucose in the combs for bee provender. It was not the comb he objected to, but feeding the bees glucose.

In his rebuttal, Dr. Wiley responded in a fashion that was to become characteristic. Not content merely to defend himself, he also wished to correct the evil he criticized. To this end he reminded the beekeepers that his report to the Indiana State Board of Health had shown how to prevent adulteration. Convinced of his sincerity, the beekeepers of the United States became enthusiastic Wiley supporters.

In 1880 came permission to study the manufacture of glucose at a factory in Peoria, Illinois, while a guest at the home of the owner. This brought knowledge of every step in the process of making glucose from the conversion of starch into a mixture of dextrin and dextrose. Though believing glucose had its legitimate uses, he insisted adulteration was not one of them.

In 1882, largely through Dr. Wiley's publication on sugar, an Indiana company was formed to introduce the culture of sorghum and the manufacture of its syrup. Farmers were persuaded to plant sorghum to insure supplies for the company mill. Profits increased each year from the very first as processes of manufacture became improved. These activities were of course sandwiched between teaching at Purdue and weekend teaching of chemistry at the Medical College. The tenure at Purdue was pleasant; marred only by censure for riding a bicycle through the streets of Lafayette and playing baseball with students. An offer to resign was hastily refused.

Nevertheless, Dr. Wiley felt somewhat hampered by the restrictions of a faculty career. His growing interest in foods and his basically practical outlook demanded a wider application. With the year

High-wheeler bought by Dr. Wiley in 1880. Preserved
at Purdue, photograph was made on January 29, 1957.

1883 came an increasing desire to sever purely academic connections.
Moreover, the work with sorghum had attracted such favorable
comment as to bring an appointment as Indiana delegate to a convention of sorghum growers, together with an invitation to address
the meeting the same evening as Dr. George B. Loring, Commissioner
of Agriculture. It was a historic evening for the introduction to Dr.
Loring eventually resulted in Dr. Wiley's appointment as chief
chemist in the Department of Agriculture and his turbulent career
as purefood crusader.

CHAPTER III

The Golden Era

THE CIRCUMSTANCES and conditions which led to Dr. Wiley's appointment as chief chemist of the Department of Agriculture were unusually fortuitous; they could hardly occur again. It required a rare combination of favorable influences to place at the head of chemical investigation for the United States the ideal man, one who combined superlative training with character and diligence. Until the forces of greed and corruption unseated Dr. Wiley the Bureau of Chemistry became one of the most unique institutions in the history of human affairs. Nothing like it has ever been known and nothing like it will probably ever be known again.

The first happy circumstance was the recognition of his ability by Norman J. Coleman, an enterprising editor interested in development of the domestic sugar industry. It was he who was instrumental in arousing the favorable interest of Dr. Loring, the Commissioner of Agriculture. This gentleman was above thinking along political lines and because of his own scientific outlook, immediately recognized Dr. Wiley's exceptional competence when he heard him speak.

Not only were the involved personalities brought together through ideal influences, but the time was particularly opportune. There was an urgent desire to develop the domestic sugar industry both for the benefit of the farmer and the manufacturer. This project required direction by an impartial and competent scientific agency. Obviously if a commercial interest were to be the guiding spirit in developing the sugar industry, it would be promoted purely selfishly. Scientific discoveries would be kept secret to shut off competition. Under government auspices, the scientific discoveries related to sugar processing would be available to all those interested in investing their capital and a monopoly would thereby be avoided.

The chemistry division of the Department of Agriculture therefore became something far more than a routine investigating bureau —a scientific institution of the first rank. This was due above all to Dr. Wiley's remarkable qualifications and personality, which made him the ideal public official.

First of all was the sense of duty engendered by his parents which recognized obligations so conscientiously. All through his career he was cognizant only of being a servant of the people and that he must work for the interests of the public only. It was therefore inevitable that those who eventually defeated Dr. Wiley recognized in his incorruptible honesty a threat to their illicit aims. After Dr. Wiley, the Food and Drug Administration was controlled by powerful interests which not only protected them against their own violations of the Pure Food and Drug Act but made it impossible for anyone not in the inner circle to do business. Such was the perversion and corruption of the intent of the Pure Food Act which Dr. Wiley protested so vigorously in his *History of a Crime*.

Besides Dr. Wiley's magnificent personal characteristics, every feature of his life, from his boyhood on the farm to his scientific training, contributed in some way to his versatility. On the farm, he learned how food was grown and harvested; how it was prepared and preserved for future use. He acquired an incorruptible taste for pure and wholesome foods and his later insistence on unbolted and undegerminated flours was propounded not from book learning but from actual knowledge of superiority through taste and consumption. Later as more and more debased food products were introduced to replace the wholesome foods he knew, Dr. Wiley could confirm the evidence of his taste with laboratory tests.

As a teacher, Dr. Wiley had acquired the knack of imparting his knowledge to others. It enabled him later to train competent and loyal assistants. He was able to explain his ideas lucidly to the public, to legislators, to business men, by reducing complex chemical problems to simple and plain language. Self-training in writing out speeches and then committing them to memory also contributed to the excellence of both his literary style and his speaking delivery.

Combine all this versatility with scientific training equal to the finest available—from studying with some of the greatest authorities in the world—and it comprises a stupendous list of qualifications. It meant that Dr. Wiley could hold his own, and did, in scientific dispute with any authority in chemistry. To sum it up— since it was inherent for Dr. Wiley to give every problem or task the utmost of his ability and to go far beyond just the ordinary fulfillment of his duties—it was only natural that the Bureau of Chemistry became more than just a government office, evolving into a scientific institution of the highest caliber.

When Dr. Wiley first assumed his duties in 1883, food processors and manufacturers had things practically their own way. Knowledge of food chemistry was in its infancy and there were few restrictions on the use of chemical preservatives of all kinds. Secure in their freedom, the food interests probably paid little attention to the new chief chemist in Washington. Today of course the appointment of a disinterested official in a position of such importance would be impossible. The food interests have their powerful lobbies and influential connections and can usually prevent the appointment of anyone who they suspect would be too harsh. Their long warfare with Dr. Wiley in which they were often defeated proved the danger of an independent and fearless public official.

At first, Dr. Wiley was but a political appointee, subject to the vagaries of changes in administration. Despite an election the coming year, he immediately plunged into his work, oblivious to the uncertainties of his position. Dr. Collier, his immediate predecessor whom Wiley praised as a chemist "of keen intellect, fine technique, and enthusiastic tenacity—", had entertained the idea that the sorghum plant could supply the entire sugar needs of the country.

Dr. Collier enthusiastically advanced this idea, establishing numerous experimental fields around Washington to grow the plant and making thousands of chemical analyses of the sorghum sap in his laboratory. Dr. Loring was not convinced that the experiments were proving fruitful and frowned upon concentrating so much effort on only one project. This difference of opinion led to the dismissal of Dr. Collier. However, it had been decided upon before

the appointment of Dr. Wiley and he was in no way responsible for
it, nor had he sought the post.

Dr. Collier became angered by his dismissal and in retaliation
attacked Dr. Wiley personally. He instituted strong efforts to regain
his position, and used his influential political and editorial connections in this campaign. The bitterness and unfairness of the
printed attacks hurt Dr. Wiley deeply but after answering with a
few articles of his own he decided to ignore them and remain silent.

This proved a wise policy for President Arthur supported both
him and Dr. Loring. Eventually Dr. Collier's campaign was defeated
and he was appointed to head an agricultural experiment station with
the understanding his attacks would cease. The Collier incident was
Dr. Wiley's first baptism under political fire and a forerunner of
what he was often to encounter in his future career. Unfortunately
he was not always to be awarded the fine support of his superiors
that he first experienced in the Golden Era of his first years in
Washington.

On examining Dr. Collier's work, Dr. Wiley decided his unsatisfactory results were due to the variety of sorghum grown around
Washington. He believed a sorghum plant indigenous to a semiarid
region would probably be better able to supply the type of sugar
needed for large scale production.

The hardy sorghum plant had a deep growing network of roots
capable of thriving in dry regions where less suitable plants would
fail to mature. Portions of Nebraska, Kansas and the foothills of
the Rockies were ideal for growing sorghum. Experimental stations
in those regions were established in the quest to produce sugar from
sorghum in commercially profitable quantities.

In 1884 President Arthur was succeeded by Grover Cleveland,
which of course brought the possibility of being replaced as chief
chemist. Fortunately President Cleveland appointed Norman J.
Coleman as Commissioner of Agriculture—the very gentleman who
had recommended Dr. Wiley in the first place. Disregarding his
Republican affiliations, Mr. Coleman refused to make a change in
spite of the efforts of influential politicians who coveted Dr. Wiley's
post as a political plum.

It was truly the Golden Era for as Dr. Wiley wrote autobiographically he found in Mr. Coleman "a most amiable and delightful

gentleman. He was an enthusiastic devotee of agriculture. He believed in doing the right thing at the right time, and he endeared himself to all chiefs of bureaus and divisions who served under him. So far as I know he did not make a single change in any responsible office by reason of political needs."

Besides sorghum, the possibility of securing sugar from beets was also being investigated. Professor McMurtrie of the University of Illinois who had once served as chief chemist, had laid the foundations for the beet sugar industry. He was a very co-operative gentleman, supplying Dr. Wiley with all the information of his preliminary researches at his command. With this help, the project of producing beet sugar was greatly advanced and resulted in the publication of the first of a series of bulletins from the Bureau of Chemistry on the beet sugar question.

While all this was going on, there was of course an increasing need for investigating the alarming practices in food adulteration. In addition to sugar research, the first ten years of Dr. Wiley's tenure as chief chemist also were devoted to continuing examinations of food products for evidence of adulteration. From 1887 to 1902 the famous *Bulletin 13* on food adulteration and preparation of foods was published.

The sugar question, however, was one of prime importance for industrial reasons. For the benefit of the sugar industry, the Bureau of Chemistry published a map of the areas proven most advantageous and profitable for beet cultivation. The Bureau also endeavored to increase the amount of sugar derived from cane in Louisiana and other Southern areas, which produced only about 120 pounds to the ton.

Dr. Wiley attributed the low production to imperfect extraction of sugar juices by the milling process then in vogue. He believed that the diffusion process of the European beet sugar industry could be more fruitful—and spent about six months in France, Germany and Spain studying that method.

Upon his return, the Bureau of Chemistry secured authorization to build experimental stations at Fort Scott, Kansas and a Louisiana plantation on the Mississippi delta. Though diffusion production was encouraging, the volume was not sufficient to be commercially profitable. Fort Scott extracted almost total sugar from sorghum but failed at obtaining the necessary crystalization. An experimental station completely divorced from commercial production and devoted entirely to purely scientific research was then decided upon.

It was set up at Medicine Lodge, Kansas under the provisions of a special appropriation from Congress, together with permission from the Internal Revenue Department to set up a still to recover the alcohol used as a precipitant. Dr. Wiley credited the idea to Walter Maxwell, one of his assistants.

This method proved a booming success. Five-sixths of the alcohol used as a precipitant was recovered and crystalized sugar at the rate of 200 pounds per ton was obtained from the residual sirup by evaporation and dehydration. This achievement crowned the years of fruitless research and experimentation and proved conclusively it was possible to extract practically all the sugar from cane and sorghum. The benefits to domestic agriculture could be incalculable. Unfortunately they have never been adequately realized.

With the administration of President Benjamin Harrison came probably the most glorious period in the Golden Era of Dr. Wiley's government service, as far as sympathic support from his immediate superior was concerned. The new Secretary of Agriculture was Governor Jeremiah Rusk, who treated Dr. Wiley almost like a son, so pleasant and ideal was their relationship.

They traveled together, especially on trips related to the sugar industry. Secretary Rusk also expanded the work of the chemical laboratory and extended its range of investigations until they covered not only foods but drugs and beverages. He elevated the various divisions of the Department of Agriculture such as Animal Industry, Plants, and Chemistry to bureau rank. Under Secretary Rusk's inspired leadership, these bureaus made important advances in their work.

Secretary Rusk was the last of the sympathetic superiors Dr. Wiley was to know; the Golden Era was passing. Malicious influences started their work and the long struggle against corruption began with the return of President Cleveland to office. Evidently the splendid work in encouraging the domestic sugar industry had aroused antagonism, for the new Secretary of Agriculture, J. S. Morton brought with him a decided bias against sugar research.

He purported to see that work as only a form of corruption and graft and quickly ordered the experimental stations abandoned and the machinery, supplies and buildings sold at a fraction of their value.

Not content with this, Secretary Morton ordered an investigation to unearth evidence of graft in ordering equipment and supplies. Obviously this was the first attempt to discredit Dr. Wiley, in this case possibly inspired by the sugar trust which found it impractical to set up a monopoly in so vast a country as the United States with its high standards of living. Sugar growing could be better controlled in a country with peon labor, under a semifeudal system subsisting principally on one crop. A domestic sugar industry therefore was to be stringently opposed.

The investigating committee could find only one charge to lodge against Dr. Wiley after several months of probing: that of transporting a jug of whiskey, presumably for his private use—though he did not drink—at an expense to the government of twenty-five cents.

It was of course typical of Dr. Wiley that he was only amused by these tactics and believed that Secretary Morton was sincerely mistaken. He did not attribute any sinister design to his tactics, though it could well be in order. The gentleman was too intelligent in other respects to be opposed to scientific research. His ideas on agriculture were very sound and he was also an earnest advocate of forest conservation, Arbor Day being rightfully named in his memory. His deliberate wrecking of the extremely meritorious work of the Bureau of Chemistry on sugar research is undoubtedly part of the commercial buccaneering that blackens the history of the United States.

Dr. Wiley had influential friends, among them Clifford Richardson, his first assistant, who was not only a highly qualified chemist and scientist but socially prominent in Washington. He had been a classmate of Theodore Roosevelt with whom he remained on excellent terms during his Presidency, while also remaining loyal to Dr. Wiley, who did not enjoy Theodore Roosevelt's blessings.

In addition to his official duties, Dr. Wiley was active in organizing together with Dr. McMurtrie the American Chemical Society. In 1892 Dr. Wiley was elected to the presidency and re-elected the following year. He watched the Society grow in prestige and membership from year to year and helped considerably in its growth.

During this period, when he was making such immense contributions to chemistry both through his government work and his professional associations, Dr. Wiley was content with only a modest salary, and never asked for an increase. The chairman of the Appropriation Committee knew how modest it was. Noticing an item of $2,500 for the pay of a "scientist," he recognized it as just the amount Dr. Wiley also received.

"What is a scientist?" he asked.

"A scientist," Dr. Wiley observed, "is a man who can make two dollars grow on an appropriation bill where only one grew before."

This greatly amused the chairman of the Appropriation Committee and also called to his attention the many-sided talents of Dr. Wiley, who was equally at home in his administrative work or in his laboratory. Observing how Dr. Wiley fought for suitable compensation for the scientists in the agriculture department while he as chief chemist received no more than his assistants, the chairman of the Appropriation Committee decided to allow two dollars remuneration to grow where there was only one before. He doubled Dr. Wiley's salary and it remained at $5,000 per annum until he left government service.

That, too, was part of the Golden Era—the conscientious legislators who also saw in Dr. Wiley a public official of unparalleled integrity and competence. Many of them stood by him steadfastly when the storm clouds gathered and the era of controversy, of constant battling against predatory and unscrupulous interests, fraud and chicanery became more and more intensified. The tempo of American life was speeding up and with the accelerated pace came high-pressure advertising and selling, false claims and counterfeit substances, adulterated foods, fakery and packaging to conceal spurious contents.

CHAPTER IV

Fathering the Pure Food Law

THE McKINLEY administration began to bring the food controversy to a boil. James Wilson was appointed Secretary of Agriculture and held the post longer than any other man—for 16 years and through four administrations. Dr. Wiley wrote of him:

> I look back upon the fifteen years I spent as his subordinate in the Department of Agriculture and cannot withhold the conviction that he had the greatest capacity of any person I ever knew to take the wrong side of public questions, especially those relating to health through diet.

But was Wilson's opposition based on perversity or ignorance or was it formed out of sympathy for various food interests? As in the case of Secretary Morton, who had wrecked sugar research, such bigotry was not characteristic of either gentleman. Their actions could have been dictated by a powerful but invisible influence. A man in public office could not risk antagonizing public opinion unless there was some important obligation involved.

In James Wilson's case, his deep concern for the sanctity of business and his respect for the investments of the food interests without considering the public health, indicates alliances and sympathies impossible to renounce. What a contrast Harvey Wiley presented with his sincere devotion to the ideals and principles so inherently a part of his being.

In his crusade for health-giving foods, Dr. Wiley gradually began to enlist the support of the pubic whose welfare he was so anxious

33

to serve. His battle was in essence a struggle against private and selfish interests on behalf of the public. It is a tribute to his extraordinary competence, sincerity, and diligence that he emerged a victor in that struggle, for his opponents were powerful indeed. Only a man of unparalleled courage could have dared to face the deadly enmities and the virulent antagonisms he aroused. Only a man of outstanding virtues could also have fired the imagination and enlisted the support of so many zealous admirers. Among the press, in the Halls of Congress, on the Supreme Court, among club women, farmers, and the chemical profession Dr. Wiley had sincere and devoted friends.

Numbered among his supporters were Edward Bok, William Allen White, and Norman Hapgood, all editors of the highest prestige. To the list of his friends must also be added the names of many of his students and colleagues, some of whom had become officials in the food and agriculture departments of various states. Among these were Ladd of North Dakota, Allen of Kentucky, Barnard of Indiana, Frear of Pennsylvania, Scovell of Kentucky, and Weber of Ohio.

In a sense, the battle was touched off by the publication of the famous *Bulletin No. 13* of the Bureau of Chemistry which covered adulteration in practically all classes of foods. Later, as the scope of Dr. Wiley's investigations broadened, he began stepping on more and more sensitive toes. The list of violators of the public welfare through debasing, mislabeling, and misrepresenting foods, beverages, and drugs became longer and longer. With it, lengthened the roll of the enemies of the Bureau of Chemistry—determined to throttle its authority. Among them were sugar interests, canners, the fruit industry, liquor rectifiers, flour millers, meat packers, and the patent-medicine fraternity. They developed a phalanx of opposition, fighting every proposed measure with deadly ferocity.

One event that stirred up strong public opinion was the "embalmed beef" scandal touched off by Major-General Miles during the Spanish-American War. The greed of the packers in forcing their decayed and rotted meats upon our soldiers was a crime that outraged the nation. Though a court whitewashed the packers, during the investigation it was testified the Army beef was identical to that served the public. This startling disclosure aroused the public.

Newspapers and magazines then began to conduct their own examinations of foods offered for sale to the public.

In 1899 the New York *Herald* found adulteration in 40 common food products. The impurity of spices was discovered to be almost universal; finding a pure and unadulterated spice or condiment in an ordinary grocery was virtually impossible. Miss Alice Lakey, chairman of the food investigating committee of the Food Consumer's League, made a quilt of flannels dyed in the various hues and produced by the very same anilines used to color foods. Dr. Shepard, state chemist of South Dakota, framed the following menu to show how any family in the United States could easily take forty doses of chemical preservatives in one day:

BREAKFAST

Sausages containing coal tar dye and borax.
Baker's bread containing alum.
Butter containing coal tar dye.
Canned cherries containing coal tar dye and salicylic acid.
Pancakes containing alum.
Syrup containing sodium sulphate.

DINNER

Tomato soup containing coal tar dye and benzoic acid.
Corned beef and cabbage with saltpeter.
Corn scallops with sulfurous acid and formaldehyde.
Canned peas with salicylic acid.
Catsup with coal tar dye and benzoic acid.
Vinegar with coal tar dye.
Mince pie with boric acid.
Pickles with copperas, sodium sulphate, and salicylic acid.
Lemon ice cream with methyl alcohol.

SUPPER

Bread and butter with alum and coal tar dye.
Canned beef with borax.
Pickles with copperas, sodium sulfate, and formaldehyde.
Catsup with coal tar dye and benzoic acid.
Lemon cake with alum.
Baked pork and beans with formaldehyde.
Vinegar with coal tar dye.
Currant jelly with coal tar dye and salicylic acid.
Cheese with coal tar dye.

Dr. Ladd, of the North Dakota Department of Agriculture, reported finding from 5 to 15 grains of boric acid to every pound of ham and dried beef he analyzed. In hamburgers, steaks, and sausages the amounts ranged from 20 to 50 grains per pound. When prescribed as a medicine the maximum dosage allowed by physicians was only 10 grains per day.

Why were these chemicals put in meats? The answer was obvious: to destroy any offensive smell and taste, thus robbing the consumer of his best means of self-protection. Sardines often marked "Packed in olive oil" were badly decayed and the oil which preserved them never had any contact with olives. Vinegar was commonly made with acetic acid, which is a preparation formed through the destructive distillation of wood. For only two cents, a gallon of vinegar could be manufactured with a trace of malic acid or concentrated apple juice added to give a chemical reaction imitating the genuine article.

Some of the most vicious outrages were perpetrated on children to rob them of their pennies when buying candy. Dr. La Wall, the eminent pharmacologist and editor of the *U.S. Pharmacopeia*, analyzed many samples of candy sold to children at school stores. He found as common ingredients burnt umber sold as pure and lard stearin with a melting point of 135 degrees F., whereas the body temperature is only 98.6 degrees. Furniture glue, dangerous ether flavoring matter, paraffin, shellac, and other injurious substances were also ingredients of the candies sold to young children with an effect on their growing and sensitive organs and tissues that can be imagined. To continue the gruesome inventory—Dr. La Wall found lampblack used in coloring licorice, marshmallows blued with ultramarine, and poisonous sulfuric acid in molasses candy with glucose, shredded coconut, and other ingredients. A child spending his penny could get four doses of one of the deadly sulfites the cleaners use as whiteners.

The most outrageous frauds were the work of the patent-medicine fakers, of whom Dr. Wiley wrote in his *autogiography*:

> In the whole sordid review the most wretched and disgraceful evil the pure food and drug law sought to remedy was that of "patent" medicines with the various nostrums, salves, appliances, poisons, magic, and sheer

fraud this group of ghouls foisted upon the suffering humanity of that period. . . . So-called "tonics," bitters and elixirs were riding upon a high tide of popularity. Most of these nostrums were nothing more nor less than alcoholic drinks, and they created appetites in the poor dupes who used them as vicious as drunkards craving for rum. . . . The nostrums glibly guaranteed to "cure" the microbe in whatever form he might be found. Germs and bacteria replaced the microbe in the public interest and "medicines" sallied forth to attack germs and bacteria. . . .

Of course most of the quack medicines which afflicted that generation were positively harmful in their effects. The "headache powders" were quite uniformly drugs, and vicious habit-forming drugs at that. Women and girls became addicted to their use in tragic numbers. The pain-killers and pain-relievers usually depressed the heart of the victim who used them and the reaction made the pain far worse. Poisonous "women's remedies" were sold in amazing quantities and the sum total of their harmful effects will never be known. Poor mothers doped their babies into insensibility at night with soothing syrups containing opium or morphine. Catarrh cures, depending on cocaine and opium for their efficacy, had a rushing sale. . . . Cancer "cures' flooded the market. . . . Consumption, of course, offered a fertile field for exploitation. Patients with tuberculosis were usually willing to spend the last cent obtainable to recover their health, and the friends who preyed on them many times got their last cent in exchange for a mixture of cod-liver oil and poisonous drugs.

Another powerful group was the whisky "rectifiers," catering to the enormous thirst of the American public and unrelentingly hostile to any form of regulation. In most cases the rectifier concocted a mixture of raw alcohol, artificial color and flavor blended to simulate genuine whisky, brandy, or rum. These interests were tremendously affluent, having almost limitless financial resources to spend against enactment of restrictive laws—controlling as they did over 80 per cent of the nation's distilleries.

Add to the ranks of patent medicine fakers and liquor rectifiers, the fruit processors using sulfur dioxide and coloring materials to simulate tree-ripened fruit; the flour interests using bleaches and milling processes to rob their products of the last vestige of nutri-

DR. WILEY IN HIS CELEBRATED LABORATORY

tional quality; the manufacturers of "corn sirup" which was nothing more than pure glucose; and the soft-drink purveyors borrowing their techniques and trickery from the patent-medicine fraternity. United they comprised the culprits who were not only inflicting untold damage upon the health of the nation but foisting upon the public tasteless, inert, and unappetizing foods and beverages.

The unique services of Dr. Wiley did not merely consist of exposing the frauds being perpetrated; they went much further than that. Under his capable direction the Bureau of Chemistry not only pointed out the evil, but also suggested an alternate and beneficial procedure. In one case Dr. Wiley tried to persuade an Indiana ketchup manufacturer that benzoate of soda was not only unnecessary but destroyed flavor and palatability.

With some hesitation the ketchup processor agreed to produce a batch without using benzoate, though fearful of bringing about an explosion by allowing fermentation to proceed unhindered. When an explosion failed to occur, he sent a mixed case of both benzoate treated and untreated ketchup to a favored customer and asked him to compare the taste. The customer was so delighted with the excellent flavor of the untreated ketchup he reordered immediately. Convinced, the processor assured Dr. Wiley some time later he was certain that benzoate of soda was wholly unnecessary and actually had only debased his product.

The use of sulfur dioxide for treating wines and dried fruits was also proved to be superfluous and harmful to palatability. Dr. Bigelow, Assistant Chief Chemist whom Dr. Wiley often praised in the highest terms for his competence, demonstrated how ordinary brine in a weak solution not only could preserve the color of dried fruits, but also retained the delicious flavor which sulfur fumes inevitably destroyed. Dr. Bigelow's paper proving his point was never allowed publication and to this day is no doubt gathering dust in the files of the Department of Agriculture.

Dr. Wiley's unusual array of talents was thoroughly tested in those stormy years of battling so valiantly for a new food law. Resentment was particularly high against him among members of the Western Packers' Canned Good Association whom he was scheduled to address at its convention in Atlantic City in February, 1906. Incensed because they believed Dr. Wiley's proposed legislation would work great hardships upon them, the canners were in a violent mood. Afraid of a possible lynching, the president of their association met Dr. Wiley at his train from Washington and implored him to cancel his speech and return. Turning back was of course out of the question and Dr. Wiley insisted on fulfilling his engagement.

That evening when he appeared, this was the man the canners saw before them, as described by Mark Sullivan:

> On the platform, the forcefulness and originality of his utterances gained from the impressiveness of his appearance. His large head capping the pedestal of broad shoulders and immense chest, his salient nose shaped like the bow of an ice breaker, and his piercing eyes compelled attention. He had a keen instinct for the dramatic.

In an atmosphere of tenseness and hostility, Dr. Wiley gently began:

> "Is there a man in this audience who would take a dollar from his neighbor's pocket? If so, raise your hand."

Not a hand was raised. In the same refrain, he asked:

> "Is there a man in this audience who would so adulterate, so degrade, and so misbrand a package of his goods as to cheat the consumer out of a dollar of his money when he bought that package? If so, hold up your hand."

Again not a hand was raised. One man clapped in approval. The applause spread and the audience, won over by Dr. Wiley's sincerity, dropped its hostile attitude to listen respectfully. He devoted his address to the practices in the canning business which a pure food law could correct and vastly improve. The changes, he assured them, would not only be of immense benefit to the health of the public but would increase their profits and protect them against the competition of inferior and dangerous food products.

Interrupted only by applause, Dr. Wiley spoke for over an hour. At the end, he was accorded a unanimous vote of thanks. Because of his speech the canners reversed their position and began to lend their support toward the enactment of a pure food law. This support eventually hastened its passage, as Dr. Wiley acknowledged.

But the greatest and most dramatic demonstration of the harm in preservatives was the organization of the "Poison Squad" in 1902.

Up to that time Dr. Wiley was comparatively unknown to the general public. The interest aroused in his daring experiment, one of the most valuable and scientifically authentic ever performed in the history of nutrition, brought national and international renown.

The Poison Squad experiment is probably the most graphic example of the Bureau of Chemistry's invaluable service to science and the public. It proved that the Bureau was far more than just a government agency; it had become a scientific and educational institution of the first rank.

The organization of the experiment was highly scientific. The squad was assembled for a test which only human subjects could provide—laboratory animals being unsatisfactory for many reasons, of which the greatest was the lack of a check on the psychological factors involved. Animals possessed only one superiority as subjects for test by providing autopsies of the histological and pathological changes in their organs. To offset that were many disadvantages because of physiological differences, uncertainties as to comparable dosages, and the effects of environment and activity.

Organization of the Poison Squad required a special Act of Congress which authorized the Secretary of Agriculture "to investigate the character of food preservatives, coloring matters, and other substances added to foods, to determine their relation to digestion and health, and to establish the principles which should guide their use."

Twelve healthy young men in the Civil Service volunteered to take the first series of tests. They pledged themselves to eat only what was prescribed for them at the kitchen and dining room set up in the basement of the Bureau of Chemistry and not to depart from their usual hours of work, sleep, and recreation. A physician was detailed to examine them periodically for any signs of developing symptoms.

The men were first fed rations of unadulterated foods to establish their individual nutritional requirements for maintaining normal weight and physical well being. Their excreta were also collected during this period for chemical analysis, which gave a complete check on the normal metabolic efficiency in utilizing food.

When this information was compiled, the experiment began. Borax was the first preservative added to the diet of the Poison

Squad. The amount added was kept constant and maintained until the subjects began to complain or show evidence of digestive impairment. When such evidence developed, the test was terminated immediately.

The impairment could be attributed to the chemical additive because it was the only variable in the experiment—the normal diet having been established for the maintenance of their health while their usual activities had remained stabilized in every respect. Further proof of the effect of the additive was in the amelioration of symptoms as soon as the subject was rested from further ingestion for ten days. In many cases, ten days proved insufficient to restore normal physical well being. However, at the end of 40 days, a complete release for another forty days was allowed to remove the last vestige of any effects from ingesting the additive.

In the borax experiment, 7½ grains were added to the daily diet— which was a much smaller amount than usually consumed in commercially prepared foods. For the first 15 or 20 days the subjects displayed no visible effects and went about their activities without discomfort. After that, their appetites began to fail until it was impossible for most of the subjects to consume normal rations. Persistent headaches accompanied by depression and debility were manifested in every case. It also became necessary to administer borax by means of capsules as otherwise the young men would not knowingly eat any food containing it.

The experiment with borax was continued for nine months and the subjects then permanently released. It took several months of rest for complete relief. The next chemical tested was salicylic acid— upon an entirely new squad, as one year was about the limit of human endurance for submission to the tests. Practically the same results were obtained with salicylic acid, and were also confirmed with all the other additives tested during the five years of Poison Squad experimentation.

During those years the dining table in the Bureau's basement became the most publicized in the world. Dr. Wiley became famous. The imagination of the public was fired. Reporters flocked around the Poison Squad and stimulated public interest further. Every little detail received overwhelming attention by the press. When capsules were added, a poet wrote:

SONG OF THE PIZEN SQUAD

On prussic acid we break our fast; we lunch on morphine
    stew;
We dine with a matchhead consomme, drink carbolic acid
    brew;
Corrosive sublimate tones us up like laudanum ketchup
    rare,
While tyrotoxicon condiments are wholesome as mountain
    air.
Thus all the deadlies we double-dare to put us beneath the
    sod;
We're death-immunes and we're proud as proud—Hooray
    for the Pizen Squad!

The chemical and physiological data collected were voluminous and a valuable addition to the science of nutrition. From the mass of figures and statistics, an ominous conclusion could be drawn: if additives could so markedly affect the health of robust and virile young men, what would they do to women, children, and invalids? The public pondered this question and began to understand. The clamor for a pure food law increased to a bellowing roar.

Commencing in 1889, for many years pure food laws had been introduced in Congress, only to be sidetracked. Usually they passed in the house of their origin, only to fail to pass in the other. Year after year the powerful lobbies managed to block passage of new laws. But the cumulative effect of the food scandals and the resultant publicity, together with the growing prestige and influence of Dr. Wiley, could not be withstood. Late in 1905 "A Pure Food and Drug Act" was introduced by its author, Senator McCumber of North Dakota. The usual attempts to foil its passage began. The Senator from North Dakota, however, notified his colleagues that the law had become the paramount desire of the public and he threatened to tell the entire country of their devious methods to sidetrack this imperative bit of legislation.

The gigantic power of the interests against pure food legislation was launched to attack the bill when it was finally introduced. Committee rooms to hear their complaints were jammed with attorneys for the whiskey rectifiers, the patent-medicine fraternity, and the canners, all pleading for exemption from the provisions of the new law. Their plaint was that the law was insane and too harsh. They dolefully predicted their ruin.

In his *History of a Crime,* Dr. Wiley gave an admirable summary of the testimony rendered before the Committee on Interstate and Foreign Commerce. There was an impressive array of experts, all asserting that additives in controlled amounts were harmless and absolutely necessary for food preservation. One so-called expert testified that in North Dakota and Berlin, two areas where preservatives had been banned from foods, statistics showed the death rate had tripled. Needless to say, no such figures existed.

All kinds of arguments, pleas, and suggestions were tendered. The manufacturers sought to have a clause included that knowledge of the deleterious effect of a substance had to be established to convict a food processor. This would of course have completely nullified the law as proof of guilt would be impossible to obtain. Assured of public support, the proponents of the Pure Food Law refused to compromise.

One of the most steadfast supporters of the bill was James R. Mann, a Congressional Representative from Illinois and member of the investigating committee. Each day he secured information from the Bureau of Chemistry which enabled him to refute and contradict the claims and assertions made by the affected interests in the hearings. Mann proved to be a valuable ally for he threw himself into the fight to secure passage of the law with vigor and determination.

The chairman of the Committee granted to Dr. Wiley the privilege of summing up the entire controversy. His testimony ran into many hours of cross-examination and many printed pages of text. One by one he met the arguments of the pleaders and dissected them expertly and brilliantly. In his testimony before the Committee on Interstate and Foreign Commerce, Dr. Wiley was at his superlative best in explaining the work he had performed for so many years and in summarizing his unremitting efforts to secure protection for the public against the unregulated and unconscionable practices of so many of the food interests.

This passage, demolishing the argument that certain types of chemical additives exist in a natural form in foods and on this account their use is justified, is particularly illustrative of his argumentative skill:

The weakness of this argument is so apparent that only a few of the causes of the fallacy need be mentioned. Hydrocyanic acid, perhaps one of the most poisonous organic acids known, exists in minute traces in the fruit of peaches and plums, associated often with benzaldehyde, a flavoring agent. It exists in some varieties of cassava in such proportions that fatal effects have resulted from eating the cassava starch. Salicylic acid is present in a flavoring product known as oil of wintergreen and may exist in traces in other food products . . . Arsenic is a widely distributed poisonous material which is often found in our foods, due to absorption from the soil. The presence of these bodies, instead of being a warrant for using more of them, points to the necessity of reducing their quantity to the minimal amount necessary.

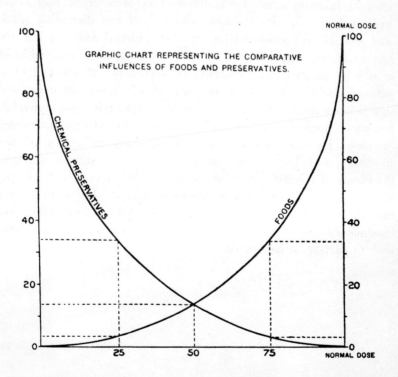

GRAPHIC CHART REPRESENTING THE COMPARATIVE INFLUENCES OF FOODS AND PRESERVATIVES.

Another penetrating refutation of the fallacy of arguing that slight doses of additives were harmless, was illustrated (as above) to compare the effects of foods and preservatives. Assuming the lethal dose of a food to be zero, since death occurred through starvation, and the lethal dose of a drug or chemical additive at 100, Dr. Wiley showed how their actions were diametrically opposed. If the lethal dose of one was the normal dose of the other, then the harmlessness of a drug was a wholly illogical and unmathematical argument which his chart illustrated so clearly.

When the Committee went into executive session to draw up the Pure Food and Drug Act in its final form, Dr. Wiley sat with it. In its final shape, the bill incorporated essentially every finding and suggestion of the Bureau of Chemistry. It authorized the Bureau to seek indictments for any violations of the Act and made it the supreme scientific authority for determining such violations.

So strong was public sentiment in favor of the bill that dissident interests failed to secure the addition of any amendment that would weaken its power. Its passage, with only a few dissenting votes, was probably the greatest triumph of enlightened democracy in the history of the United States. It proved that inspired leadership of a man of incorruptible integrity, of superlative ability and competence could bring about reforms of the most dramatic and significant nature. It was a triumph of principle over powerful, predatory interests. And though to be sure the victory was never complete, because the cunning and insidious influences of the interests affected eventually found means to circumvent the law, the legacy of scientific food lore which Dr. Wiley bestowed through his many achievements can never be destroyed. His work in the Bureau of Chemistry and his writings before and after his incumbency are a treasure which can forever enrich those who wish to partake of its benefits.

CHAPTER V

The Law Becomes Perverted

AFTER THE Pure Food and Drug Act was passed, to the credit of many ethical and public-spirited food processors there was a sincere desire to obey it—regardless of any former opposition. For the most part food and drug firms made no organized attempt to defeat the law. Undoubtedly they realized a fair and just statute would protect them from illegal and fraudulent competition as well as benefit the health of the public.

Unfortunately there were others still strongly opposed and bent on sabotaging the law. The technique of defeating it was developed to a fine art which eventually secured almost complete domination over the law's administration. The passage of the Act forced the interests to realize a fair and impartial Bureau of Chemistry posed a threat to their profits. Because for all practical purposes Dr. Wiley was the Bureau of Chemistry, they concentrated upon him.

First they tried to get him to change his views on food adulteration. Naturally this failed. Indirect bribery was also attempted by offering him a lucrative position as consulting chemist to the whiskey industry. This offer, through their chief legal counsel, Dr. Wiley characterized as:

> . . . clumsy and ludicrous in its arrangements. If I had accepted the fee as consulting chemist for this organization I should have been an easy victim to their dictation.

During the balance of 1906, hearings were held in various cities preparatory to the law's going into effect on January 1, 1907. At these hearings, the usual querulous plaint against financial ruin was raised. At sessions in New York the fruit packers sent their delegates to protest against the ban on sulfur. Later that evening one delegate somewhat shamefacedly sought out Dr. Wiley at his hotel. He confessed coming at the urgent behest of his wife, who was decidedly opposed to chemicals to treat fruits and refused to allow such food on her table. His confession was imparted to the other members of the committee the following day as an example of how a man could be forced into opposing a measure he knew was absolutely just.

When the interests saw it was useless to attack Dr. Wiley as an individual, they adopted another tactic. In the person of Mr. McCabe, legal solicitor for the Department of Agriculture, they found an ally who had a strong influence with Secretary Wilson. One morning, out of the blue, a Professor Dunlap was appointed as Dr. Wileys' chief assistant, without having taken a Civil Service examination nor having proved his competence. He was also to serve on a newly formed Board of Food and Drug Inspection which would include Solicitor McCabe and Dr. Wiley as well.

It was a rank flouting of the new law, which had not authorized any such body but had invested complete authority in the Bureau of Chemistry to rule on the purity of foods and their proper labeling. The purpose of the illegal board was obviously to hamstring the new law. Dr. Wiley was overruled in every case and became a mere figurehead. The Bureau of Chemistry no longer could pass on adulteration or misbranding and its chief found it impossible to proceed against any infraction of the Act, particularly when patent-medicine bottlers and whiskey rectifiers were concerned.

Anxious to continue the use of benzoate of soda, saccharin, alum, and glucose sanctioned in the name of "corn sirup" the interests quickly sensed a glorious opportunity also to secure immunity. They sent a delegation to President Theodore Roosevelt to petition for some other authority besides the Bureau of Chemistry to rule whether or not their products were injurious.

After hearing them, President Roosevelt scheduled another session the next day to which Solicitor McCabe, Secretary Wilson, and Dr. Wiley were also summoned. At this session—a dramatic highlight in the life of Dr. Wiley—the large group of tycoons and their counsel reiterated their well-known complaints and pleas, prophesying ruin if prohibited from using preservatives and manifesting their hostility to the "unreasonable" attitude of Dr. Wiley. After hearing them out, the President turned to Secretary Wilson to ask his opinion on the use of additives.

In that instance, the Secretary loyally supported Dr. Wiley. When the President asked Dr. Wiley to answer the complaints he cited his work with the Poison Squad which proved the harm in additives. Whereupon the President bared his teeth in his famous way, struck the table a resounding thump, and growled, "You shall not put this substance into foods."

Apparently the cause of pure foods had won a smashing victory, but it soon proved only a fleeting triumph. Continuing in their pleas, the delegation called attention to the fact that saccharin, which saved one processor "four thousand dollars last year," was now prohibited. At this point, Dr. Wiley committed a *faux pas*. Impulsively he condemned saccharin as an injurious substance, before being asked his opinion. This was not only a breach of etiquette before the mighty but it touched the President's own life because his own doctor was prescribing saccharin for him.

"Anyone who says saccharin is injurious to health is an idiot," he growled to Dr. Wiley.

The session abruptly ended on this note. The consequences proved dire for the cause of pure food because President Roosevelt soon afterward appointed another Food and Drug Board. Its head was Dr. Remsen, the very man who claimed to have discovered saccharin —which alone should have disqualified him from presiding or sitting on such a board.

Dr. Remsen and his Board were part of the moves, schemes and plots that Dr. Wiley stigmatized as "The Crime Against the Pure Food Law." The Remsen Board's decisions were the deadliest and most crippling blows for they nullified practically everything the Bureau of Chemistry had achieved and completely usurped its functions. Instead of prohibiting chemical additives, they permitted them in almost unrestricted amounts.

The press and the public were wholeheartedly with Dr. Wiley and opposed to the Remsen Board. Condemnation of the hamstringing of an enlightened law enacted only after twenty-five years of unremitting effort and public education was almost universal.

The Remsen Board imitated the Poison Squad experiments with various additives but failed singularly to observe proper controls. Their subjects were allowed to eat any quantity of food they wished, whereas Dr. Wiley had first established each man's normal ration to maintain his weight, physical well being, and usual activities. The Remsen Board experiments discredited Dr. Wiley's findings in every case except the use of sulfate of copper in canned vegetables. As a consequence, borax, the salicylates, and all other chemical additives which Dr. Wiley had proved so conclusively were deleterious were regarded as harmless and no restrictions were put upon their use.

Another reprehensible activity of the Remsen Board was to send their experts to Indiana to testify against an action to bar adulterated products from being sold in the state. Employees of the Bureau of Chemistry, however, were forbidden to testify for the State of Indiana, certainly a glaring case of rank partiality and misuse of public funds as the so-called testifying experts were paid by the Board out of its appropriation.

Indiana took its case to the United States Supreme Court and secured subpoenas for the testimony of the Bureau of Chemistry; Dr. Wiley ignored Solicitor McCabe's order forbidding such testimony and supported the stand of the State of Indiana in court. On the witness stand, his assistants attested they had been forbidden to testify. The Supreme Court upheld the right of the State of Indiana to enforce its Pure Food Law, which was modeled after the federal statute. This decision led to dissolution of the Remsen Board but not before it had inflicted irreparable harm to the cause of pure foods.

Executive decrees also emasculated the Pure Food and Drug Act. President Taft personally nullified virtually every restriction against whiskey rectifying and sanctioned coloring, adulterating, and misbranding of liquors. This edict of the President, signed by both the Secretaries of Agriculture and Commerce, restored everything the rectifiers had lost in the courts. It was no longer even necessary for them to fight such cases, for by executive proclamation they were allowed what the courts had consistently outlawed. Consequently, exemptions the patent-drug vendors, the canners, and the fruit packers had gained by crippling the authority of the Bureau of Chemistry were also achieved by the whiskey interests.

Another instance of unscrupulous interference was perpetrated by the German representative of the aniline dye industry. He was sent to the United States by the cartel to modify Dr. Wiley's aversion to permitting its use in coloring foods. When he called at the Bureau, the chemist representing the aniline dye cartel made no attempt to justify its use but instead craftily hinted that if Dr. Wiley would abandon his position against the use of aniline food colors he would secure his election to preside over an International Congress of Applied Chemistry the coming year.

Needless to say, Dr. Wiley's refusal was blunt and brutally frank but the incident was typical of the brazen practices prevalent. Not only did domestic interests flout the law, but a foreign cartel had the effrontery to attempt to bribe an official of the United States Government to allow their poisons to be freely spread on our foods.

For more than five years after the enactment of the Pure Food Law, Dr. Wiley doggedly fought for its proper enforcement despite the disheartening odds against him and the sabotage inflicted from all sides. He was also compelled to defend himself against personal attacks and was constantly shadowed by detectives. Important *Bulletins* were suppressed and he was further burdened with the animosity of the Secretary of Agriculture as well as the hosts of interests arrayed against him. Though a good portion of the press and a great majority of the public were with him, the forces of greed and cupidity working directly in Washington, employing the most expensive legal talent and the most cunning lobbyists, were too much. Dr. Wiley saw the Pure Food and Drug Act, brought into being by the sincere and idealistic effort of a quarter-century, degenerating into a printed regulation, possessed of neither life nor direction, brazenly flouted by every interest it was intended to curb.

The intent of the Act was changed to one of instruction rather than enforcement. Whenever a flagrant violation was unearthed, the food processors involved were gently instructed how to correct their infraction by the Department of Agriculture through the agency delegated to enforce the law. When it is recalled that practically all

U. S. DEPARTMENT OF AGRICULTURE,
BUREAU OF CHEMISTRY—BULLETIN No. 84, PART I.
H. W. WILEY, CHIEF OF BUREAU.

INFLUENCE OF FOOD PRESERVATIVES AND ARTIFICIAL
COLORS ON DIGESTION AND HEALTH.

I.—BORIC ACID AND BORAX.

By H. W. WILEY, M. D.,
WITH THE COLLABORATION OF W. D. BIGELOW, CHIEF OF THE DIVISION OF FOODS,
AND OTHERS

WASHINGTON:
GOVERNMENT PRINTING OFFICE.
1904.

U. S. DEPARTMENT OF AGRICULTURE,
BUREAU OF CHEMISTRY—BULLETIN No. 84, PART II.
H. W. WILEY, CHIEF OF BUREAU.

INFLUENCE OF FOOD PRESERVATIVES AND ARTIFICIAL
COLORS ON DIGESTION AND HEALTH.

II.—SALICYLIC ACID AND SALICYLATES.

By H. W. WILEY, M. D.,
WITH THE COLLABORATION OF W. D. BIGELOW, CHIEF OF THE DIVISION
OF FOODS, F. C. WEBER, AND OTHERS

WASHINGTON:
GOVERNMENT PRINTING OFFICE.
1906.

"Poison Squad" *Bulletins*

of the chemicals formerly prohibited had again found their way to a pseudolegal use, these infractions could hardly have been trivial.

Another instance of sabotage of the magnificent work of the Bureau of Chemistry was suppression of the following *Bulletins*, whose titles alone convey their significance:

Corn Sirup as a Synonym for Glucose (1907).
Sanitary Conditions of Canneries (1908).
Reprint of Part LV on Benzoic Acid and Benzoates (1909).
Medicated Soft Drinks (1909).
Drug Legislation in the United States (1909).
Food Legislation to June 30, 1909 (1910).

U. S. DEPARTMENT OF AGRICULTURE.
BUREAU OF CHEMISTRY—BULLETIN No. 84, PART III.
H. W. WILEY, CHIEF OF BUREAU.

INFLUENCE OF FOOD PRESERVATIVES AND ARTIFICIAL
COLORS ON DIGESTION AND HEALTH.

III.—SULPHUROUS ACID AND SULPHITES.

By H. W. WILEY, M. D.
WITH THE COLLABORATION OF W. D. BIGELOW, F. C. WEBER AND OTHERS.

WASHINGTON:
GOVERNMENT PRINTING OFFICE.
1907.

U. S. DEPARTMENT OF AGRICULTURE.
BUREAU OF CHEMISTRY —BULLETIN No. 84, PART IV.
H. W. WILEY, CHIEF OF BUREAU.

INFLUENCE OF FOOD PRESERVATIVES AND ARTIFICIAL
COLORS ON DIGESTION AND HEALTH.

IV.—BENZOIC ACID AND BENZOATES.

By H. W. WILEY, M. D.
WITH THE COLLABORATION OF W. D. BIGELOW CHIEF OF THE DIVISION
OF FOODS, F. C. WEBER AND OTHERS.

WASHINGTON:
GOVERNMENT PRINTING OFFICE.
1908.

"Poison Squad" *Bulletins*

Estimation of Glycerin in Meat Preparation (1910).
Technical Drug Studies (1910).
Experiments on Spoilage of Tomato Ketchup (1911).
Influence of Environment on Sugar Content of Cantaloupes
(1911).
A Bacteriological Study of Eggs in the Shell and of Frozen
and Desiccated Eggs (1911).
The Arsenic Content of Shellac (1911).

Though the sabotage was successful, the deadliest blow to the Food
and Drug Act—directed at Dr. Wiley himself—was yet to be hurled.
Even if robbed of most of his rightful authority, as head of the

Bureau of Chemistry he was always a formidable opponent. By ousting him, victory over the food law would be final and complete.

Dr. Wiley was charged with misuse of public funds on the pretext that he had engaged an expert at a higher salary than allowed per diem—although actually lower than the annual stipend. Various bureaus of the government had always resorted to the practice, which was in no way unusual and actually was economical. It is illustrative

International News Service

Before testifying at Moss Committee Hearings: From left to right: L. F. Kebler (Division of Drugs), Dr. Wiley, H. H. Rusby, and W. D. Bigelow (Division of Foods).

of the desperation of his enemies when they could dig up nothing more serious.

The Moss Committee, formed to investigate the preposterous charge, completely exonerated Dr. Wiley. However, the committee did find that the Remsen Board had illegally expended over $175,000 of public funds in various attempts to defeat the Pure Food Law, such as sending experts to testify against the State of Indiana.

Though exonerated, Dr. Wiley found that his accusers were in no way censured for their previous illegal tactics nor for their waste of public funds entailed in investigating the unfounded charge against him. That was too much. On March 15, 1912 Dr. Wiley summoned reporters to his office and announced his resignation, summarizing the events and circumstances which had brought about emasculation of the Pure Food and Drug Act. First was nullification of the provision that the Bureau of Chemistry was empowered to examine all suspicious foods and refer all cases of misbranding and adulteration to the courts. The various boards and executive orders which usurped this power granted to the Chemistry Bureau by the law prevented prosecuting any such violations.

As a consequence, practices which the law meant to prohibit were sanctioned and in Dr. Wiley's resignation he wrote:

> A few of the instances of this kind are well known. Among these may be mentioned the manufacture of so-called whiskey from alcohol, artificial colors, and flavors; the addition to food products of benzoic acid and its salts; of sulfurous acid and its salts; of sulfate of copper, of saccharin, and of alum; the manufacture of so-called wines from pomace, chemicals, and colors; the floating of oysters often in polluted waters for the purpose of making them look fatter and larger; the selling of moldy, fermented, decomposed, and misbranded grains; the offering to the people of glucose under the name of "corn sirup," thus taking a name which rightfully belongs to another product made directly from Indian corn stalks.

Convinced he could accomplish more as a private citizen in the activity closest to his heart, Dr. Wiley proclaimed his intention to continue his fight for pure foods free of the harassments which had plagued him since enactment of the law he had fathered.

The resignation created quite a commotion. It was ironic, but in spite of the tremendous following Dr. Wiley enjoyed—the support of enlightened newspaper editors, food manufacturers, and federal and state officials—a powerful minority had finally engineered his separation from government service.

After his passing, the Bureau of Chemistry became just another government agency. It was no longer a scientific and educational institution on a par with the finest research organizations or university departments. The zeal, the competence, and the high principles of its Chief had given it a prestige and standing unique and everlasting—yet it had functioned solely in accordance with genuine democratic principles.

Decay and deterioration in the Bureau after Dr. Wiley abdicated resulted from domination of the Department of Agriculture by the interests he had fought. They manipulated adminstration of the law purely for their own profit. In 1929, when Dr. Wiley could contain himself no longer at the sad spectacle, he published his protest— *The History of a Crime Against the Food Law*—to tell the world how the Pure Food and Drug Act which was intended to protect the health of the people was perverted to protect adulteration of foods and drugs.

Dr. Wiley published the book himself as evidently the material was too explosive for a commercial publisher. A virtual suppression ensued and the book became unprocurable for a long time; here or there by diligent search a copy could be secured. In 1955 the original edition was reproduced by photolithography and is now available. (See Bibliography, page 161).

CHAPTER VI

The Legacy

THE CAREER of Dr. Harvey W. Wiley in government service is in itself a great part of the legacy he left to the world for it is an incomparable example of meritorious service. His administration of the Bureau of Chemistry provides a standard of procedure for effective enforcement of the Pure Food Law which must stand forever as an ideal goal. If we were to seek another Harvey W. Wiley to duplicate his achievements he would necessarily need these prerequisites:

His competence would be comparable to almost any chemist in the world, whether the head of a research foundation, the department of a university, or employed in industry. He would possess the personality to command the respect and admiration of his co-workers and inspire them with his own zeal and integrity. He would be able to perform nutritional experiments of the finest delicacy and accuracy—on human beings whenever possible—and report the results with absolute impartiality.

In addition, such a man would have the delightful knack of imparting his ideas in such simple, straightforward fashion as to render them understandable to those lacking technical or scientific training. He would not only be able to judge the merits of a food or processing method for its nutritional value but on finding it unacceptable could also suggest an alternate and acceptable procedure.

Most important, another Harvey W. Wiley would be able to detect in any proposed article for popular consumption the slightest possibility of danger to public health and to quickly institute proceedings to bar it from commerce. His guiding principle would be to serve only one master—the public welfare. Infractions of the intent and purpose of the Pure Food Law would be quickly prosecuted not only to safeguard public health but to protect ethical members of the food industry from unfair and illicit competition.

Had Harvey Wiley been able to fulfill his life's ambition, this is what he would have achieved:

> No food product of our country would have any trace of a synthetic chemical preservative; no soft drink any caffein or theobromine; no bleached flour would be manufactured. Our foods and drugs would be wholly without any form of misbranding or adulteration. The health of our people would be vastly improved and their life greatly extended. The manufacturers of our food supply, and especially the millers, would devote their energies to improving the public health and promoting happiness in every home by the production of whole ground, unbolted cereal flours and meals.

> The resistance of our people to infectious diseases would be greatly increased by a vastly improved and more wholesome diet. Our example would be followed by the civilized world and thus bring to the whole universe the benefits which our own people had received.

> We would be spared the ignominy and disgrace of great scientific men bending their efforts to defeat the purpose of one of the greatest laws ever enacted. Eminent officials of our government would escape the indignation of out- raged public opinion because they permitted and en- couraged frauds on the public. The cause of a wholesome diet would be the goal of the Food and Drug Administra- tion and the crimes against the Pure Food Law would be swiftly halted.

If history repeats itself and there is a coming of a second Dr. Wiley, he will need the loyal and sincere support of the public, enlightened newspaper editors, government officials and bureau assistants. His task, unfortunately, will be even more difficult than his predecessor's, for he will arrive on the scene when the interests he necessarily must oppose are infinitely more powerful than they were in 1883 and exercise an insidious influence in the most vital branches of our government.

In fact, the prospects of ever seeing another Harvey W. Wiley in Washington are dim indeed. Rightly, we should be extremely grateful that he ever happened at all without expecting miracles to be repeated. His career and achievements actually arose through a series of extremely fortuitous circumstances. It was pure luck that Dr. Wiley's abilities were recognized by high government officials and he was placed in exactly the right post at almost exactly the right time, when the coteries that eventually displaced him were unaware of the threat to chicanery and fraud that he represented.

That the existence of a Doctor Wiley was an almost miraculous circumstance can be surmised from the fact that no comparable figure ever arose in other fields, despite urgent and imperative needs. There arose no comparable scientist and government official in agriculture to halt the appalling abuse of our lands by destroying fertility and the nutritional value of crops through improper use of the soil.

Nor was there ever a comparable figure to protect the public interest in our forest lands, our mineral wealth, or in the practice of medicine which has become almost an industry instead of a profession. One could go on and on trying to discover a man of such inspired integrity and high intelligence in industry, commerce, finance, or law. Scan all these fields and try to recall one man who fought so zealously for the public welfare with such little concern for self. The only comparable figures to Dr. Wiley are men who engaged purely in research and scientific discovery—such as Darwin, Harvey, Newton, or Einstein. No other man in history ever successfully carried out scientific work of lasting merit while at the same time compelled to fight the forces of evil and corruption treacherously sniping and sabotaging his work, accusing him of malfeasance, and endeavoring by hook or crook to nullify his efforts.

Within two weeks after he departed from the unbearable atmosphere which enveloped him, Dr. Wiley was back at the work closest to his heart—food investigation and nutritional education. As food editor of *Good Housekeeping* magazine, a post he accepted for its appeal to his interest in the public welfare, he was free from the continual harassment of his enemies and assured of the support and good will of his employers. He was provided with an excellent laboratory for food testing, editorial space to publicize his findings, and authority to pass on acceptability of food and drug advertising.

In many essentials, the work was an extension of his duties as Chief Chemist for the United States Government. The parallel was remarkable, for not only did the doctor continue to examine hundreds of different food and drug products but his editorial work was little different from the preparation of government bulletins.

Even authority was not lacking for besides the power to accept or reject advertising his recommendation or disapproval of various products carried considerable weight from an economic standpoint. Read as he was by millions who respected his judgment, the Wiley stamp of approval was a great asset for any product.

Dr. Wiley's writings subsequent to his government career may rightfully be considered as comparable to his published *Bulletins*, of which he wrote or collaborated in over 400. His books read extremely well and were written primarily for the layman. These volumes (*see* BIBLIOGRAPHY, page 161), in addition to hundreds of scientific papers, government bulletins and magazine articles, comprise a valuable portion of the legacy of nutritional knowledge Dr. Wiley bequeathed to posterity.

His fundamental principle was exceedingly simple: Foods should be grown, transported, processed, and prepared for the table so that natural nutritional properties would be conserved to the highest degree. This precludes the use of toxic chemicals for preservation, flavoring, or coloring to hide the absence of original nutritional elements or presence of decay. Ideal nutriment must therefore be close to its original state, consumed almost immediately after harvesting or slaughter. Where that is impossible, the next acceptable alternative is food preserved by natural methods and subjected to a minimum of processing, transportation, and storage.

It is out of such foods, Dr. Wiley counseled, that we must build our diets. Besides being wholesome and nutritious they will be highly palatable—for the best tests of food quality are aroma, appearance, and taste. With food of that type there is no particular need to worry about balance or diet, except in cases of diabetes or other serious conditions. Only when foods have lost their inherent good qualities or are products of deficient soils must one worry about variety or vitamin supplements. In this respect, Dr. Wiley suggested:

A most important fact in connection with this discussion [food balance] is that the human animal, when he has access to foods of various kinds—in other words, in what we would call a normal condition of life—*naturally* selects a ration which is so well balanced as to require but little amendment. The departures from a reasonably well-balanced ration are due not to human selection but to the artifices of man in denaturing natural food products. The human animal who has access to nature's stores of foods does not require a trained dietitian to write a menu for him. Inasmuch, however, as a large percentage of us have access only to prepared foods, it is well to be on our guard. Not only are we likely to get an excess of fats and carbohydrates and a deficiency of proteins, but also we are in greater danger of living on demineralized foods, and thus suffering from the threatened effect of mineral starvation. Even if we eat only whole cereals, we do not get a proper balance, because of the incompleteness of the basic mineral elements and the tendency to get an excess of acidic matter (phosphoric acid).

Another fallacy Dr. Wiley ridiculed was the claim advanced that certain foods are especially suitable to nourish the nerves, blood, bones, brain, or muscles. That an abundance of calcium, minerals, trace elements, proteins, or vitamins in some foods would necessarily make them valuable to one particular system of the body is not sensible and he contended:

The mere fact that a little larger amount of these ingredients exists in one food than in another, does not necessarily indicate superiority. The element may be present in smaller amounts in other foods but in a more available form, or the food which contains the smaller amount may be eaten in larger quantities. There is a great danger of distorting and misapplying dietary figures of this kind, and they should be used with a grain of common sense and with a broad view of the subject.

Such a view Dr. Wiley held to in writing his two most extensive works, *Foods and Their Adulteration* and *Beverages and Their Adulteration*, possibly the most authentic food encyclopedias ever published. They are probably the greatest treasures in the Wiley legacy and their lines seem illuminated by the fires of many hard-fought battles for unadulterated food. These books were based principally on *Bulletin 13*.

They include many invaluable hints on detecting adulteration and selecting foods with the highest nutritional value. Such knowledge is priceless. Today it is more pertinent than ever because the list of foods which are treated in some form is endless. It is practically impossible to secure—through ordinary channels— simple, natural and unadulterated foods. The task of their selection becomes increasingly difficult today. A knowledge of what happens to food from its origin on the farm until it reaches our tables is absolutely imperative.

The same interests that dictate the administration of the Food Law also appear to dominate the dissemination of information on foods— through advertising and through subsidized articles written by so-called nutritional authorities. The simple, honest facts about foods are hard to secure unless one searches diligently. The richest source of this information is in Dr. Wiley's two classics on foods and beverages. A summary of the most important facts contained in these works should be helpful to anyone interested in securing the best in nourishment.

The principal foods from which to select a good dietary are cereals, meats, fruits, and vegetables. Since Dr. Wiley's day, fundamental practices in food technology have remained about the same. The information he supplied on foods—their development, marketing, and composition in respect to nutrition and digestibility, problems of storage and transportation, and dangers from decay and adulteration—is still as valid as ever. Moreover, the reader will discover that a review of the Wiley books will be most helpful toward understanding present conditions in the administration of the Food Law and current practices in the industry. He will probably also discover how little they have changed fundamentally and that advances in technology have only led to greater and more diversified methods of fooling the public.

CHAPTER VII

Meats, Eggs, Fish

T O FOLLOW Dr. Wiley's order, meats come first because they are usually first on the dietary and are the most popular of all foods—also the most expensive. Possibly such high prestige is a heritage from the past when the hunter was the most respected of the tribe. From time immemorial, salt, sugar, vinegar and wood smoke have been employed to preserve the meat of the hunt. These methods are still the most permissible. Ironically, modern technology has not yet furnished a worthy substitute for the old techniques.

Refrigeration of meats during storage and transportation preserves their palatability only partially. Enzymatic action continues even during refrigeration so that quick consumption is always imperative. Time definitely limits the value of stored meats, though some authorities contend that enzymatic action is beneficial during the initial storage period and aged meats have a higher nutritional content. That still remains a debatable question. Dr. Wiley held otherwise and believed the longer the period before consumption, the less the meat's value. He considered one month the limit for storage under refrigeration. We would not classify a meat as fresh after one week of storage, though possibly it would still be edible.

There are four methods of preserving meats:

1. Curing with the aid of condiments.
2. Treatment with chemicals and noncondimental preservatives.
3. Sterilization with heat.

63

Meat Cuts and How to Cook Them
BEEF CHART

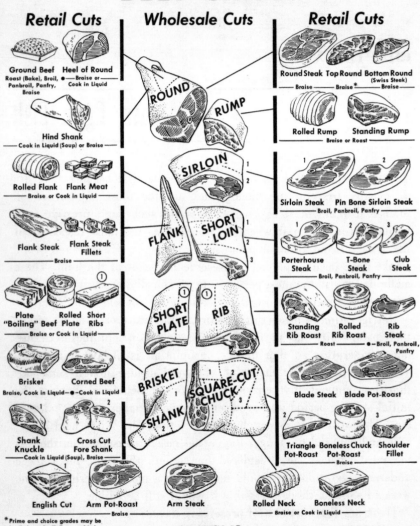

Retail Cuts   **Wholesale Cuts**   **Retail Cuts**

Ground Beef   **Heel of Round**
Roast (Bake), Broil,   ●—Braise or—
Panbroil, Panfry,   Cook in Liquid
Braise

Hind Shank
— Cook in Liquid (Soup) or Braise —

Rolled Flank   **Flank Meat**
— Braise or Cook in Liquid —

Flank Steak   **Flank Steak Fillets**
— Braise —

Plate   **Rolled**   **Short**
"Boiling" Beef   Plate   Ribs
— Braise or Cook in Liquid —

Brisket   **Corned Beef**
Braise, Cook in Liquid—●—Cook in Liquid

Shank Knuckle   **Cross Cut Fore Shank**
— Cook in Liquid (Soup), Braise —

English Cut   **Arm Pot-Roast**
— Braise —
    Arm Steak

ROUND   RUMP

SIRLOIN

FLANK   SHORT LOIN

SHORT PLATE   RIB

BRISKET   SQUARE-CUT CHUCK

SHANK

Round Steak Top Round Bottom Round
(Swiss Steak)
— Braise —   Braise *   — Braise —

Rolled Rump   **Standing Rump**
— Braise or Roast —

Sirloin Steak   **Pin Bone Sirloin Steak**
— Broil, Panbroil, Panfry —

Porterhouse Steak   **T-Bone Steak**   **Club Steak**
— Broil, Panbroil, Panfry —

Standing Rib Roast   **Rolled Rib Roast**   **Rib Steak**
— Roast —   ●—Broil, Panbroil, Panfry

Blade Steak   **Blade Pot-Roast**

Triangle Pot-Roast   **Boneless Chuck Pot-Roast**   **Shoulder Fillet**
— Braise —

Rolled Neck   **Boneless Neck**
— Braise or Cook in Liquid —

*Prime and choice grades may be
broiled, panbroiled or panfried

COURTESY OF
NATIONAL LIVE STOCK AND MEAT BOARD

4. Drying in the sun and air as practiced by primitive peoples, which is the best preservative method of all.

Of the four, only treating meats with chemicals and noncondimental preservatives is objectionable. Commercial considerations rather than food value dictate such a method.

Properly cured meats have an aroma and taste which is distinctive and appetizing. Curing not only prevents decay but imparts the pleasant flavor of the condiment and favors the development of enzymatic action in the meat. Unfortunately, curing by the traditional method is comparatively expensive and slow. Economies can be effected by the use of chemical substitutes and mass production.

This brought on practices which the Pure Food Law attempted to correct, such as quick-aging and the use of less expensive noncondimental substances. Germicides impart neither taste nor aroma but by preventing formation of organic ferments in meats make preservation more certain and less expensive. Actually, meat so preserved is no longer food but a tasteless substance whose remaining nutritional value is destroyed by the chemicals used to preserve that value.

In reality, these so-called preservatives retain only the color and appearance of freshness, without hindering the most dangerous changes from continuing despite them. The most common chemicals used in meat preservation—which Dr. Wiley fought so strenuously to outlaw—were borax, boric acid, and sulfite of soda, the latter being used to preserve color. Chemically, borax paralyzes fermentative action which eliminates decay at the expense of palatability. When borax and boric acid are used to decrease costs by substituting for natural condiments, though less condiments are necessary, favorable enzymatic action becomes inhibited. In the various ways meats are offered commercially, adulteration is always possible though often entirely unnecessary. Pickled meats for example can be preserved in vinegar quite well, yet sulfite of soda or boric acid is often used. Their presence must of course be stated on the label.

Sterilizing and then canning meats is potentially the best commercial method of preservation. Unfortunately, canning also permits the inclusion of inferior meats. The consumer should be wary of those treated with saltpeter, which is most commonly used in canned tongues and hams, as is also, on occasion, boric acid.

Meat Cuts and How to Cook Them
VEAL CHART

Retail Cuts
Wholesale Cuts
Retail Cuts

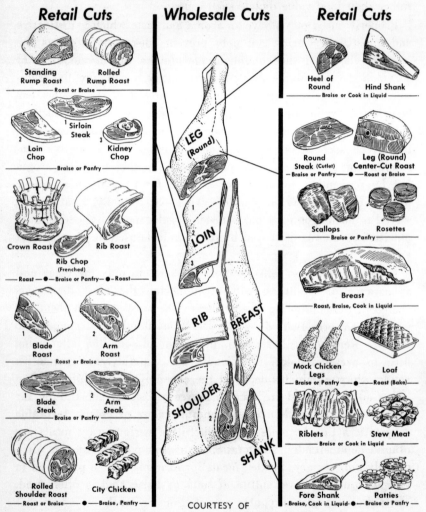

Standing Rump Roast — **Rolled Rump Roast**
— Roast or Braise —

1 Sirloin Steak
2 Loin Chop — **3 Kidney Chop**
— Braise or Panfry —

Crown Roast — **Rib Roast**
Rib Chop (Frenched)
— Roast — ● — Braise or Panfry — ● — Roast —

1 Blade Roast — **2 Arm Roast**
— Roast or Braise —

1 Blade Steak — **2 Arm Steak**
— Braise or Panfry —

Rolled Shoulder Roast — **City Chicken**
— Roast or Braise — ● — Braise, Panfry —

LEG (Round)
LOIN
RIB — **BREAST**
SHOULDER
SHANK

Heel of Round — **Hind Shank**
— Braise or Cook in Liquid —

Round Steak (Cutlet) — **Leg (Round) Center-Cut Roast**
— Braise or Panfry — ● — Roast or Braise —

Scallops — **Rosettes**
— Braise or Panfry —

Breast
— Roast, Braise, Cook in Liquid —

Mock Chicken Legs — **Loaf**
— Braise or Panfry — ● — Roast (Bake) —

Riblets — **Stew Meat**
— Braise or Cook in Liquid —

Fore Shank — **Patties**
— Braise, Cook in Liquid — ● — Braise or Panfry —

COURTESY OF

NATIONAL LIVE STOCK AND MEAT BOARD

It is important to realize that by mixing good meats with impure, diseased, or unwholesome varieties, detection of adulteration is impossible through chemical analysis. Even the identification of different meats by histological examination is impossible, as under the microscope beef, lamb, or pork cannot be distinguished from each other. Once meats are prepared and canned, adulteration perpetrated by including inferior meats cannot be controlled or detected.

Starch has often been employed as an adulterant in sausages and prepared meats. This use of starch is reprehensible as it leads to nutritional imbalance in the diet. Starch in sausages also increases weight and prevents shrinkage after cooling.

In sausages and prepared meats, borax, boric acid, sulfite of soda, and benzoic acid—all proven deleterious—are still in use despite the advisability of their rigid exclusion. In addition to these preservatives, dyes are also used to impart an attractive color. The bright red of "hot dogs" today is of course the work of a dye. These dyes are coal tar products and, although certified by the FDA, should be avoided.

In addition to dyes which impart their own color, dyes can also indirectly color meats by retaining the hue which would be lost by age. Saltpeter and sulfite of soda are dyes which have no color of their own but preserve the color in hamburger and similar meats.

Lard, unfortunately, is also easily adulterated with beef fat, cottonseed oil, and stearin—a form of lard with a low melting point. Combining beef fat—which has a higher—and cottonseed oil—which has a lower—melting point than pure lard results in a mixture which approximates a correct melting point. Cottonseed oil is cheaper and brings a higher profit. Stearin, it will be remembered, was exposed as an ingredient used in candy; it has a melting point so much higher than body heat as to be indigestible.

In recent years, vegetable oils in place of lard have been coming into greater and greater use. They have many advantages over lard, including greater economy (except in the case of olive oil), better control of processing, less danger of springing from diseased sources, and fully as great a nutritional value.

Meat juices and extracts, Dr. Wiley found, offered the greatest opportunities for adulteration and counterfeiting. Each firm prepares its own product under close secrecy to guard formulas. Fancy and

Meat Cuts and How to Cook Them
PORK CHART

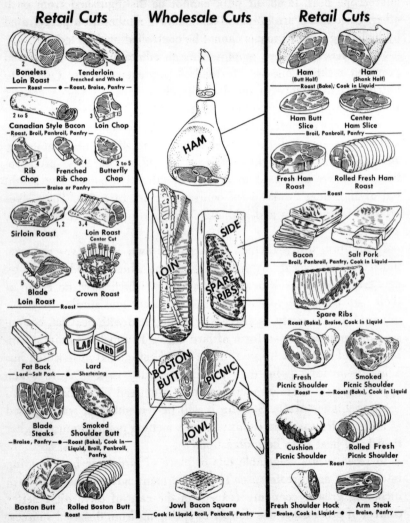

Retail Cuts

Boneless Loin Roast
2
— Roast —

Tenderloin
Frenched and Whole
1
— Roast, Braise, Panfry —

Canadian Style Bacon
2 to 5
— Roast, Broil, Panbroil, Panfry —

Loin Chop
3

Rib Chop
4

Frenched Rib Chop
4

Butterfly Chop
2 to 5
— Braise or Panfry —

Sirloin Roast
1, 2

Loin Roast
Center Cut
3, 4

Blade Loin Roast
5

Crown Roast
4
— Roast —

Fat Back
— Lard—Salt Pork —

Lard
— Shortening —

Blade Steaks
— Braise, Panfry —

Smoked Shoulder Butt
— Roast (Bake), Cook in Liquid, Broil, Panbroil, Panfry —

Boston Butt

Rolled Boston Butt
— Roast —

Wholesale Cuts

HAM

LOIN

SIDE

SPARE RIBS

BOSTON BUTT

PICNIC

JOWL

Retail Cuts

Ham
(Butt Half)

Ham
(Shank Half)
— Roast (Bake), Cook in Liquid —

Ham Butt Slice

Center Ham Slice
— Broil, Panbroil, Panfry —

Fresh Ham Roast

Rolled Fresh Ham Roast
— Roast —

Bacon

Salt Pork
— Broil, Panbroil, Panfry, Cook in Liquid —

Spare Ribs
— Roast (Bake), Braise, Cook in Liquid —

Fresh Picnic Shoulder
— Roast —

Smoked Picnic Shoulder
— Roast (Bake), Cook in Liquid —

Cushion Picnic Shoulder

Rolled Fresh Picnic Shoulder
— Roast —

Fresh Shoulder Hock
— Braise, Cook in Liquid —

Arm Steak
— Braise, Panfry —

Jowl Bacon Square
— Cook in Liquid, Broil, Panbroil, Panfry —

COURTESY OF
NATIONAL LIVE STOCK AND MEAT BOARD

misleading brand names are used and often such articles are stored for indeterminate periods. Yeast can be used to adulterate meat extract; alcohol included as a preservative and coloring matter has also been found. Salt is added in such excessive quantities as to make it a convenient way to sell salt at fancy prices.

As meat juices and extracts are primarily intended for invalids, commercial varieties cannot afford the assurance of quality and safety of home preparation of meats whose quality and freshness is known. Even home-prepared extracts, however—pure as they may be—are overrated and are the most expensive form of nourishment known.

Meat juices and extracts were extensively promoted by Liebig, the great German chemist who investigated the effects of washing and boiling meats. Liebig proved that water extracted all the soluble mineral elements from meat, rendering its liquor far more nutritious than the meat itself. His extracts enjoyed an international vogue and reaped a sizable fortune for him. Modern experiments have consistently confirmed the truth of his contentions. Laboratory animals fed a diet of washed hamburger meat will quickly die, whereas those maintained on meat whose mineral salts have been retained thrive. Adulteration extensively practiced with extracts is another instance of how scientific discoveries can be perverted to reap exorbitant profits.

All in all, meats are extremely expensive, because even the best forms of meat are one-half inedible. Much of the use of meat can be attributed to vanity or to old prehistoric traditions surrounding the killing of animals and the partaking of their flesh.

From the standpoint of economy, cereals have a decided advantage. They do not entail any inedible waste and sell at only a fraction of the cost of meat. They are usually almost complete foods in themselves, whereas meats are only partial foods and must be supplemented. Scientific nutrition therefore establishes the superiority and economy of cereals—particularly wheat—over meats.

In recent years the rising cost of beef, pork, and mutton has encouraged formation of an immense poultry industry. Raising chickens is Big Business; flocks are huge, and commercial subterfuges similar to those perpetrated in other branches of the food industry have become prevalent. In Dr. Wiley's day the poultry industry was

Meat Cuts and How to Cook Them
LAMB CHART

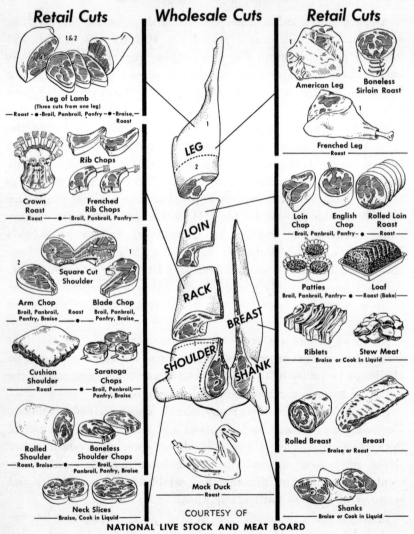

Retail Cuts

Leg of Lamb
(Three cuts from one leg)
— Roast - ● -Broil, Panbroil, Panfry -●-Braise,—
Roast

Rib Chops

Crown Roast
— Roast —

Frenched Rib Chops
— ● —Broil, Panbroil, Panfry—

Square Cut Shoulder

Arm Chop
Broil, Panbroil, Panfry, Braise

Roast ●

Blade Chop
Broil, Panbroil, Panfry, Braise

Cushion Shoulder
— Roast —

Saratoga Chops
● —Broil, Panbroil, Panfry, Braise

Rolled Shoulder
— Roast, Braise ●

Boneless Shoulder Chops
— Broil, Panbroil, Panfry, Braise

Neck Slices
— Braise, Cook in Liquid —

Wholesale Cuts

LEG

LOIN

RACK

SHOULDER

BREAST

SHANK

Mock Duck
— Roast —

COURTESY OF
NATIONAL LIVE STOCK AND MEAT BOARD

Retail Cuts

American Leg

Boneless Sirloin Roast

Frenched Leg
— Roast —

Loin Chop

English Chop
— Broil, Panbroil, Panfry - ●

Rolled Loin Roast
— Roast —

Patties
Broil, Panbroil, Panfry - ●

Loaf
— Roast (Bake)—

Riblets
— Braise or Cook in Liquid —

Stew Meat

Rolled Breast

Breast
— Braise or Roast —

Shanks
— Braise or Cook in Liquid —

in its infancy, although forced feeding to accelerate weight production was already in vogue. Flocks are no longer the part-time avocation of the farm housewife but an industrial enterprise.

One of the great arguments of the past was whether or not to draw the entrails after killing poultry. Toxic matter in the viscera and entrails was believed to permeate the meat through osmosis. In the days when poultry was not inspected too extensively, the condition of fowl offered for sale was often scandalous and the poor quality was attributed to undrawn entrails poisoning the carcass. Whether this is true has not been definitely determined. Only in kosher establishments, where religious ritual demanded killing live chickens by blood letting, was it possible to secure any guaranty of freshness. Today other evils have crept into the processing and sale of chickens, and will be described under current practices.

The student of foods will find an excellent summary of the essential facts about eggs in Dr. Wiley's classical study. Eggs carefully candled, washed, and kept under refrigeration are most desirable as food. Unfortunately, eggs entail hazards because fowl are unclean and microbes can sometimes penetrate the shell, rendering the egg extremely toxic. It is well that decayed or spoiled eggs can be readily detected.

However, illicit practices prevalent in canning can also be similarly perpetrated in what is known as the broken-egg industry. Eggs are cracked and poured into barrels, and the solution preserved by the admixture of borax. This is a financial speculation—when prices are low—to keep eggs off the market until prices rise. Such use of borax is of course just as reprehensible as in meat canning, for borax may prevent the formation of bacteria but it cannot prevent enzymatic action. The changes in protein matter which produce poisonous effects can continue in the presence of borax.

No objection can be offered to the practice of storing broken eggs if only first-grade eggs are so treated, stored in cans, and frozen. As can be surmised, inferior eggs are included. Broken eggs are purchased chiefly by bakers, which provides another reason for suspecting commercially baked products.

In the section on fish, *Foods and Their Adulteration* devotes considerable discussion to various species, their value in nutrition, their habitat, nutritional constituents, flavor, and edibility. Commercial practices in the fish industry are worthy of attention. Fish usually die by suffocation, which is contrary to the principle that no animal should be used for food that has died other than by slaughter.

It would be ideal, of course, if fish were captured and placed in pools until the time they are to be eaten—a practice prevailing in high-grade restaurants and hotels. In Germany it has been customary to keep fish alive until they are sold, but unfortunately the practice never became general in the United States.

Fish caught for canning—such as herring—are immediately slaughtered, which leads one to believe that in this case canned products can sometimes be superior to those offered in fish stores. However, canning fish—particularly salmon and tuna—requires great precautions because of toxic properties quickly developing in decomposition. Sterilization is absolutely imperative when canning fish.

The preservation of fish by pickling, drying, salting, and smoking produces highly edible products. Unfortunately there are methods of smoking fish through the use of a chemical which greatly reduces the time involved. It is highly probable that genuine smoked fish are a rarity today, and the commonly offered products have been produced through fast-acting chemicals.

Nutritionally, fish is equal to meat—having little fat and a higher nitrogenous content. Fish is not a complete food, any more than meat, and requires supplementation with starches. But it has a high food value nonetheless.

In canning fish, adulteration is practiced at times by including inferior grades or even a different species. Other species have often been substituted for salmon; hake and haddock have been represented as cod. The use of preservatives, which Dr. Wiley fought to prevent is unfortunately still followed by some fish packers. Another misrepresentation is claiming olive oil as a packing ingredient for sardines, whereas linseed oil has often been detected instead.

Clams, lobsters, crabs, and other shellfish rank nutritionally with fish. Lobster contains the highest amount of glycogen, and for sweetness is only rivaled by horse meat. At one time lobsters were a drug on the market, but since the turn of the century the demand far exceeds the supply.

Shellfish, as well as oysters and shrimps, are canned extensively in the United States. The danger of contamination is just as great as with fish. Only when the flesh is immediately canned before decomposition can take place, and thoroughly sterilized, is there little danger of food poisoning.

Oysters should be prized more for their flavor and palatability than for their nutritional value, which is only fair. A delightful taste, however, is to be prized and on this account oysters have a place in the dietary. Unfortunately oysters readily absorb water and, since they are usually graded by size, adulteration by water absorption was common. This greatly reduces palatability.

One of the pure food battles was fought over the regulation that oysters should not be shipped in water, nor in direct contact with ice. At first, oyster dealers fought this ruling and obeyed somewhat grudgingly. Years later, a gentleman who identified himself as formerly head of an oyster dealer's association accosted Dr. Wiley at a railroad station. He apologized for his former belief that the ban on soaking oysters would mean ruin for his industry, as the dealers found unsoaked oysters had a taste which increased sales ten-fold!

About the only fish oils which are used for edible purposes are salmon oil and cod-liver oil. The latter—though extremely unpleasant tasting—has been considered a valuable medicine in forms of emaciation, tuberculosis, and other diseases. Cod liver contains an extremely complex mixture of oils not usually found in other fish and its value is attributed to this variety of content. Adulteration has been commonly practiced by including the oils of other fish, which is extremely difficult to detect if added quantities are not too large. The grade of the cod itself also is an important factor in quality, as inferior species yield poor oils. The best American species of cod yields as fine an oil as the highly prized Norwegian variety.

CHAPTER VIII

Milk and Milk Products

MILK IN Dr. Wiley's estimation is one of man's most wholesome foods because of its easy digestibility, high nutritional components, and its suitability in illness when scarcely any other food can be tolerated. Milk has also been subjected to more tests than any other food article.

Different breeds provide milk of differing composition. The Holstein affords a milk of about the lowest fat content while the Jersey supplies about the highest—the comparison being 3 per cent to about 6 per cent. Nitrogenous and sugar content, mineral substances, and phosphoric acid account for the 12 per cent solids in milk—about 88 per cent being water. This is the average for all breeds at all seasons.

Dr. Wiley was quite optimistic about certified milk when he wrote his tome on food adulteration, and predicted that eventually only milk of a certified quality would be sold. The opposite is unfortunately true and certified milk is a rarity. Such milk is secured from herds which are guaranteed to be free of disease by regular inspection. Their milk is also subjected to daily chemical and bacteriological examination.

These safeguards, together with the fact that certified milk is not pasteurized and essential elements therefore not destroyed by heat, make it far more nutritious—though also more expensive. Pasteurization should be regarded only as a substitute for inspection and certification of the health of the herd.

Cream is not as complete a food as milk. While containing at least part of the nutritional elements of milk, the proportion is far less because of the high fat content—usually 18 per cent. Skim milk is the residue after the removal of cream, and contains most of the protein matter and sugar as well as the mineral content of milk. It is therefore a valuable food and lacks only in fat.

Skim milk was often misrepresented as whole milk, though under its honest name it is a desirable food—as is buttermilk. Both are practically identical in content, differing primarily in taste. Buttermilk is the residue left in the churn after the making of butter. Its pleasing acid taste is due to the ripened cream from which it originates.

Buttermilk is imitated by artificially souring skim milk through the use of ferments, chiefly those producing lactic acid. This is of course misrepresentation. Bonnyclabber is milk which has become soured by lactic fermentation and solidified to the extent that the liquid will not pour. Essentially it is a natural cheese curd with the fat content on top.

The use of chemical preservatives in milk is outlawed in practically every country of the world. Milk is also very difficult to preserve with any kind of chemical and additives have been found almost useless. For a time, formaldehyde and boron compounds were used but they have since been prohibited.

Condensed milk is a substitute for fresh milk which Dr. Wiley would recommend only under the most dire circumstances, when either the milk supply is so impure as to be highly dangerous or no other milk is available. Some authorities refuse to endorse condensed milk under any circumstances because of subtle changes which take place whenever milk is processed in any way.

Dried or new powdered milk is secured by extracting all water and preserving the milk solids so that addition of water will restore the original form. The difficulty of producing powdered milk which will revert to its original character on the addition of water is in preventing coagulation in the milk solids after evaporation. The process found most practical is drying *in vacuo* at very low temperatures which prevents coagulation of the soluble portions of the milk solids.

After cream has soured, it is churned to produce butter. The crude butter thus secured is subjected to washing and seasoning processes to prepare it for market. Treatment is with water, and the "working" separates as much as possible of the curd and other nonfatty constituents of the cream. Removing these particles improves the grade and keeping qualities of butter. Butter so produced is known as natural, unsalted, or uncolored butter and, when fresh, is sweet and has an agreeable aroma and a palatability of the finest quality.

Salted butter is produced to suit the taste of those who desire it, but connoisseurs of butter usually prefer the sweet varieties. In small quantities salt does not act as a preservative but, when enough is added for that purpose imparts a disagreeable taste.

Butter is a product greatly sinned against, the chief offenses being addition of water and coloring. The latter practice is an abomination almost universally practiced today, with "certified" aniline dyes still being permitted—although Dr. Wiley regarded all such dyes with grave suspicion.

It is poor deceit for no artificial tint can satisfactorily reproduce the natural color of good butter. Cows that feed on summer forage produce a rich, yellow butter, but even in winter their butter can have a pleasing, light amber tint. Feeds enriched with carrot roots, rutabaga, yellow maize, or clover hay will enable the cow to produce a good butter even in winter.

Renovated butter is normal butter rechurned to raise its water content to the legal limit of 16 per cent. In Dr. Wiley's belief this is adulteration even if it conforms to the legal standard.

As for oleomargarine, he did not object to it when produced from neutral lard of good quality—although there is a considerable amount of deception in attempting to pass it off as butter. Coloring is permitted upon the payment of a tax; this is also an adulteration from the standpoint of nutritional purity even though legalized for the sake of revenue.

Other forms of adulterating oleomargarine were admixing egg yolks and preserving with borax, boric acid, or salt. Domestic oleomargarine was not subjected to chemical preservatives at the time but his chief objection to the product, Dr. Wiley wrote, was the ease with which a purely processed food could be manufactured from inferior products. When properly made from lard of high quality, Dr. Wiley believed oleomargarine could be a desirable food, unsuitable only for growing children.

Cheese is one of the oldest known foods, ranking in antiquity with wine. Both go back to a thousand years before Christ. It is a natural food product, though attempts have been made to classify it as an artificial food. Artificial foods are made from inedible products, combined with mixtures of compounds containing some natural foods.

That is not true of cheese, which is a natural product because it is wholly derived from milk, a natural food. Dr. Wiley also classified wine as a natural food because of its derivation from grapes, and he pointed to the similarity between the two foods in respect to the changes they underwent during fermentation—one resulting from an alcoholic fermentation and the other from lactic fermentation.

Ripened cheese undergoes a fermentative action upon its nitrogenous elements—casein, albumin, etc. Casein is transformed into a more soluble form of protein and also acquires a distinctive flavor and aroma. Various types of molds also grow in the cheese to determine its palatability and character. The final character of ripened cheese depends upon the original nature of the milk itself, the method of preparation, the type of molds and ferments active during ripening, and the period and temperature of aging and storage.

The variety of cheeses is too extensive to be discussed and is determined chiefly by the type of milk used. Roquefort is derived from goat's milk but most cheese is from cow's milk.

Misbranding as to the country or region of origin is one of the principal offenses in the cheese industry, practiced because certain areas are known to produce cheeses of better quality. Roquefort, for example, is the product of a specific region in France; cheeses from other regions have no right to be designated as Roquefort. Swiss cheese is also a misnomer, and today designates any hard, tough cheese which has a large number of holes. There can be a wide variation in taste and desirability of many products commonly sold as "Swiss" cheese.

Artificial coloring—as with butter—is also prevalent in the cheese industry and the same objections to the practice also apply. A good cheese will have a naturally pleasing tint. Use of additives is merely to cloak the inferior quality of milk used. The same aniline dyes applied to butter are utilized in the cheese industry, having been found more suitable commercially than vegetable tints such as annotto and saffron. The danger in their use is, however, considerably greater.

Fortunately cheese is never subjected to preservative chemicals which would interfere with the process of fermentation. Adulteration was once practiced by manufacturing from skim milk and adding artificial sources of fat—such as cottonseed oil, lard, and other edible oils. This was known as a "filled" cheese, and when properly labeled was permitted upon payment of a tax—as with colored oleomargarine. The taste however was so poor and so unlike genuine cheese that it could not be sold.

Nutritionally, cheese should be regarded as a condimental substance, according to Dr. Wiley, and eaten after meat because its enzymatic action is a distinct help to digestion. Well-ripened American cheeses of the Cheddar type have demonstrated a digestibility rate of over 90 per cent of both protein and fat, which is excellent.

The practice of compounding cheeses by reducing to a paste, mixing with butter, and selling under a proprietary name has become a great industry in the United States. Today it is all but dominated by the Kraft Cheese Company. Such cheeses are not objectionable unless treated with preservatives, which is unfortunately too often the custom. Their price is also greater than natural cheeses which are intrinsically better, and the vogue of such brand-name preparations is due to triumphs of advertising.

CHAPTER IX

Cereals and Vegetables

BARLEY IS not generally used for food except in soup, although it has all the nutritive properties of the common cereals. Its chief use is in making fermented beverages.

Buckwheat, commonly classed with the cereals, is not a true grass. Its seed is prized for making bread and cake. Buckwheat flour when properly ground has a dark tint and is relished for making flapjacks. The modern product is finely ground just as is our wheat flours, and cannot be compared with old-fashioned stone-ground varieties. Nor can the old-time breakfast cakes or flapjacks from flour seeded with yeast and allowed to ferment be compared with the modern flours which contain baking powders to facilitate quick rising.

Buckwheat flour is extensively adulterated, and the common commercial varieties are only imitations usually containing rye flour, Indian corn flour, wheat flour, or other ground cereals as substitutes. Fortunately these substitutes are harmless and can easily be detected under the microscope.

Corn has almost countless varieties such as Indian corn, maize, or sweet corn, each of which differs in form and content in different localities in response to variations in rainfall, climate, or soil.

Adulteration is widely practiced in canning corn which is often bleached with burnt sulfur, sulfite or bisulfite of soda, or potash. As in the case of white flour, this bleaching is purely to cater to consumer prejudice at the expense of nutritional quality. Saccharin is also used as a sweetening agent and it will be remembered that mention of this substance in the hearing before President Theodore Roosevelt touched off the incident that eventually led to perversion of the Pure Food Act by creation of the Remsen Board.

Use of both a bleaching agent and saccharin was wholly unnecessary, Dr. Wiley contended, as only the best corn should be used without any tampering to deceive the consumer or risk injury to health. Sugar added to make ordinary corn taste like sweet corn is also to be regarded as an adulteration, as is also the addition of maize starch during canning.

Corn flour is ground commercially similarly to wheat flour with the same attending loss of nutritional qualities. The old-fashioned stone-ground corn flour is naturally to be preferred. In restaurants and hotels it is of course impossible to secure. Corn flour is so cheap it is not subject to adulteration but is itself used to adulterate buckwheat and other cereal flours.

Oats are a highly prized food both for animals and humans. The oatmeal commonly used as a breakfast food is hulled, in contrast to unhulled oats fed to horses and cattle. Oatmeals are the richest of the cereal flours both in protein and in oil. Commercial products can be highly recommended—certainly a welcome exception—for Dr. Wiley's analyses disclosed that practically all the natural nutritive qualities were retained. Adulteration is also impractical as the product is quite inexpensive.

Rice is an important food cereal of the Orient. It is rich in starch but poor in protein—suitable for those engaged in strenuous labor because it provides heat and energy. The most common adulteration practiced is coating rice with talc, paraffin, and glucose to improve appearance and provide protection against insects. These adulterants are indigestible.

Rye is more commonly used for bread in European countries than in the United States, where it is extensively used in making whiskey. It is a hardy cereal, flourishing in the same regions as wheat and other cereals. The proteins of rye correspond more closely to wheat than any other cereal, lacking only the glutenin protein found in wheat.

Rye flour when pure is dark, almost black, and is often called "pumpernickel." It can be baked long in advance of eating, and keeps well. Rye breads of lighter hue, commonly seen, are really made from a mixture of rye with wheat, barley, Indian corn, or other flours to cater to the desire for lighter colored breads.

Wheat is the most important of the cereals and grows only in temperate regions. In the United States winter wheat is planted from September to November, and spring wheat from the end of March to the end of April. There are a number of species of wheat but its quality and properties depend more upon environment than upon species. Environment makes a greater difference in wheat than perhaps in any other crop. Two great classes are distinguished —hard and soft wheat. There is a greater proportion of starch to protein matter in soft wheat. However it is the proportion of gluten to the other protein components of wheat which governs the bread-making qualities of its flour.

Gluten itself does not exist in wheat but is formed when the flour is mixed with water and two proteins—gliadin and glutenin—unite. Altogether there are five proteins in wheat but gliadin and glutenin comprise about 90 per cent of the total protein content.

About 258 pounds of wheat will produce a 196-pound barrel of flour. The bran, shorts, and screenings are sold as cattle feed and, as is well known, the best nutritional elements are in the bran which is excluded from the flour to prevent rancidity. It was the bolting of flour to screen out the bran that Dr. Wiley protested so vigorously but which is, of course, still prevalent in the milling industry.

The gluten content of flour determines its commercial value, as it permits forming loaves with a maximum water content. This does not detract from palatability. The ideal flour for baking bread contains sufficient gluten to produce a porous and spongy loaf without including too much moisture.

Flour bleaching is still in practice although at the time (1917) Dr. Wiley compiled the last edition of *Foods and Their Adulteration* he stated that bleaching of flour for interstate commerce had practically ceased. The purpose of bleaching was to permit rating inferior flours as of better quality. Adulteration—beyond bleaching— was never extensively practiced with wheat flour.

The best insurance of quality in flour is to secure it freshly ground and then bake immediately. This avoids chemical changes through fermentation and the formation of molds, as well as infestation with weavils and other pests.

Flour substitutes included can be of two kinds—nutritional and nonnutritional. Wholesome ingredients cannot be considered adulteration and bread baked with admixtures of corn meal, rye flour, or other cereal products can be desirable. However, such inert substances as finely-ground straw, bark, and nut hulls added to increase bulk—which has been practiced during famines—are frank adulterations to deceive the consumer.

Bread is generally classified as leavened or unleavened. Four leavening agents are commonly recognized:

1. Yeast.
2. Natural ferments in the flour which produce a variety of bread known as "salt rising."
3. Chemical reagents mixed into the dough.
4. Leavening reagents such as carbon dioxide or air incorporated into the dough during kneading.

Unleavened breads are crackers, biscuits, wafers, corn bread to be consumed while hot, and miscellaneous forms.

Baker's yeast causes fermentation by the action on the sugar in flour, which produces carbon dioxide and alcohol. The carbon dioxide expands the gluten to make a light and spongy mass which further expands during baking.

Spontaneous fermentation or salt rising bread is probably infeasible commercially but was once common in rural districts when home baking was practiced.

Chemical reagents mixed in the dough set free carbon dioxide. These reagents, known as "yeastcake" or baking powders, produce a light spongy loaf which would require a much longer period of fermentation with ordinary baking yeast. However, chemical residues left in the bread are objectionable, as they are inorganic and put an unnecessary strain on the excretory organs. The principal baking powders are cream of tartar, phosphate, and alum. Each leaves a residue of:

11 grams of crystallized Rochelle salts from two teaspoonfuls of cream of tartar powder.
16 grams of phosphate soda and lime from two teaspoonfuls of phosphate powder.

11 grams of sulfate of soda and hydroxide of alumina from two teaspoonfuls of alum powder.

None of these residues are beneficial. The only choice is the one the least harmful. All chemical leavening agents—including yeastcake—introduce an extraneous element into baked goods unlikely to be nutritionally desirable.

A considerable industry has grown up in the United States for the manufacture of noodles, spaghetti, and macaroni. A hard wheat is used, one that flourishes in a semiarid region on an alkaline soil. The process of manufacture is comparatively simple and rapid by forcing kneaded dough through cylinders of suitable shape. The yellow color of spaghetti is produced by placing saffron or a coal-tar dye into each batch of dough; needless to say, a wholly undesirable procedure. The strings are then cut, thrown over reed poles, and allowed to dry for a number of days—until tough enough to withstand handling without breaking.

Cake baking permits about the widest and most extensive forms of adulteration and use of inferior products and artificial substances known in food production. Good flour, sugar, eggs, and other wholesome ingredients will produce an excellent cake but all these are expensive. Commercially, artificials colors produced by aniline dyes are in common use, as are artificial flavoring essences to simulate natural ingredients.

These two are the most common forms of adulteration, but in addition stale or broken eggs preserved with borax or formaldehyde can also be used. Other dangers arise through the use of molasses containing traces of chloride of tin or of zinc salts retained from the manufacturing process. Sulfurous acid may also be absorbed from the bleaching of cane juices. All in all, commercially baked pies and cakes, unless produced by ethical firms, are most dubious foods from the evidence available.

Dr. Wiley classified breakfast foods into seven different categories and analyzed representative brands of each. He found Indian corn products quite generally very finely bolted, and considered this type of breakfast food inferior to those produced by the old-fashioned milling process. His analysis of wheat products was somewhat more favorable, although there was a great suspicion of admixture of other types of cereals.

Oat products enjoyed the best rating of all breakfast foods because commercial processing had been accomplished without material degermination, as proved by the high content of fat or oil. Products made of starch and tapioca were rated the poorest because of excessive carbohydrates. Noodles, spaghetti, and macaroni as breakfast foods were well rated due to the fact that they are manufactured from glutenous material which also guarantees a high protein content.

The products analyzed were produced under brand names and sold in package form. Dr. Wiley's chief objection to their use was from the standpoint of cost. He advocated purchasing the cereals in bulk and preparing them at home, thereby effecting not only great economies but assurance of a fresh and palatable product. Deterioration from storage and the age uncertainty of packaged products are eliminated when the purchaser buys his own cereals in bulk and prepares them fresh for each meal.

Vegetables are distinguished by high water content. According to nutritional knowledge extant just after the discovery of vitamins, vegetables were not highly regarded due to that water content—being as a rule very low in proteins. They were prized more for condimental effect and their beneficial stimulus to appetite and digestion. Today, however, many vegetables are esteemed for their minerals and vitamins. Some, such as the potato, in times of famine have been known to sustain life for long periods.

Vegetables vary markedly in keeping qualities. Potatoes and beets will keep for comparatively long periods if properly covered. Most vegetables, however, lose nutritional properties quickly, which has given rise to the tremendous vegetable canning industry. Only those vegetables which can be eaten in a raw state or which keep for long periods are not canned. From the standpoint of general knowledge which may appear rather elementary to the well informed, a few practical facts about some vegetables may be reviewed:

The beet has been produced by a process of breeding to increase sugar content from about 6 to 14 per cent. It is a palatable vegetable except for tannin, which in young and tender beets is easily removed by cooking. A white beet has been developed to produce a white sugar. Among the various beets, the garden beet of bright red color is best known.

Cabbage and beans are noted for high protein content of about two and one-half per cent. Cauliflower is quite similar to cabbage with the exception of a lower protein content. Cranberries are noted for high acidity and also for the fact that they contain a small quantity of benzoic acid. It was the presence of this acid which the food adulterants sought to capitalize upon by claiming that addition of benzoic acid in canning was only adding a substance that already existed in some foods.

The reputation and uses of garlic are so well known as to need little comment. Cows prize wild garlic which, however, gives a disagreeable odor to their milk. Horse-radish is sometimes adulterated by substitution of highly spiced aromatic turnips.

It may surprise the reader that Dr. Wiley classified cantaloupes, muskmelons, and watermelons as vegetables. Because of their high sugar content—about seven per cent—they are commonly regarded as fruits. The pea contains the highest protein content of all vegetables—about four per cent in the green pea to 27 per cent in dried peas.

Potatoes have been developed from a plant which was originally poisonous. Their high starch content is well known. The practice of spraying potatoes with arsenic is evidently an old one. Dr. Wiley considered arsenic indispensable in crop production and ventured the opinion that little if any penetrated the skins. The potato is also prized as a source of starch for laundering and sizing textiles, and for the production of alcohol. Potatoes raised for their starch content are not generally used as food. During storage, the sugar content of potatoes increases greatly—reaching five per cent; whereas in fresh potatoes the sugar content is hardly one per cent.

Sweet potatoes have many of the characteristics of white or Irish potatoes. Their sugar content is originally higher—about six per cent, and increases in storage to over 11 per cent. The starch is not used commercially, but like the ordinary potato, it is a good source of industrial alcohol, as are also yams.

In canning vegetables, the same general principles apply as in meat canning, with sterilization just as necessary to both. Vegetables also ferment through the action of either organic or inorganic elements. Such fermentation must be prevented or inhibited to preserve the nutritional qualities of vegetables.

Unfortunately many adulterations are practiced in canning vegetables. The use of saccharin and sulfites in canning Indian corn
already has been mentioned. Starch is added to produce a creamier
liquid and improve appearance. Sugar may also be added to cover
up the absence of a natural sweetness which a corn of good quality
will always possess.

In addition, adulteration from deterioration of the can is possible
if a can not in accordance with standard specifications is used. The
contents can be polluted with traces of lead, antimony, arsenic, zinc,
copper, or tin compounds. Vegetables which ferment are unfit as
food and emit a gas which markedly swells the can—although never
becoming poisonous. When the can is punctured, the escaping gas
is very noticeable.

Sulfate of copper was once added to dye peas and beans a bright
green. Its use today probably has been completely eliminated.
Saccharin is still added, and because of its synthetic nature is
distinctly injurious to nondiabetics.

Practically all adulteration in canning tomatoes has been eliminated because of greater efficiency in sterilization. The only practice
still current which can be criticized is dyeing green tomatoes a
bright red. Fortunately this practice is not very extensive. The
same is true in the manufacture of ketchup, which also would not
require dyes if made from proper materials. Benzoate of soda,
however, is considered necessary to preserve ketchup when bottles
are in constant use, as in restaurants.

Of the edible starches used principally as puddings and desserts,
tapioca is of interest because it originates in a form of the
cassava plant. As Dr. Wiley testified, this plant is exceedingly
poisonous, although the poison is quite volatile and readily disappears in cooking.

Of the many spices on the market, mustard is about the only
one which suffers from adulteration. Turmeric is often used to
impart a yellow color and disguise the addition of spices not
originating in the mustard seed.

CHAPTER X

Fruits and Nuts

FROM A dietetic point of view, fruits are significant for their sugars and acids which also account for their palatability. Their distinct aroma exudes from essential oils and compound ethers.

When properly ripened, their natural color is also very pleasing. The combination of taste, pleasing aroma, and distinctive coloring makes fruits extremely appetizing.

Fruit sugars are the common sugar (sucrose) and invert sugar containing about equal amounts of levulose and dextrose. Sugar content varies with the fruit, grapes having the highest—upwards of 25 per cent. Apples will generally have from 5 to 15 per cent sugar—pears and peaches somewhat less.

The various acids in fruits are malic in apples and its forms; citrus in oranges, lemons, etc.; and tartaric in grapes. More than one of these types as well as other acids may exist in a fruit, but the three mentioned are the principal acids in each group. In a pure state, fruit acids are not wholesome; they can on the contrary be harmful. Only in natural forms in combination with other constituents of fruits are they beneficial.

Fruits also possess a carbohydrate allied to some extent with sugar and starch but which has the capacity to jell. Known as pectin or pectose, it is common in all fruits, and nutritionally is entirely different from animal gelatin which is essentially a protein.

Fruits are valuable elements of the dietary. They have a laxative effect except in instances where excessive tannin is present, as in

some berries. Fruits belong in every diet, having valuable properties no other food can supply. However, they are subject to infection
from insects and decay from damage to their covers. Immature fruits
are distinctly unwholesome and there is always the possibility of a
spray residue remaining on the skin. For this reason cooking may
often be advisable, although it destroys some of the value of raw
fruits.

Fruit at the peak of ripeness is ideal. It then has a maximum
of sugar but when decay sets in the sugar ferments and begins to
disappear. This problem does not exist in fruits such as oranges
and berries which contain little starch and can keep for comparatively long periods.

Apples are one of our most valued and plentiful fruits. They are,
however, subject to insect infestation with the consequent spraying
which may leave arsenic traces. Apples with skins damaged in
picking, packing, or shipping suffer rapid discoloration from
oxidation. As is well known, subsequent decay can quickly spread
to other apples in the container. Unfortunately the practice of
sulfuring dried apples was carried on—though wholly unnecessary,
as proved in the case of apricots. Sulfur is harmful for its effect on
red blood corpuscles which are greatly reduced in number after
absorbing it.

Of the tropical fruits, the most abundant and important is the
banana. It is usually picked green and allowed to ripen in transit
and storage. Its abundance and cheapness accounts for the fact that
it can be shipped from great distances and still be sold at a price
within universal reach. Bananas have less waste than most fruits
and can be eaten not only raw, but cooked in various ways. As in
other starchy fruits, the starch decreases and turns to sugar as the
banana ripens. Its percentage of protein is low—just over 1 per
cent; but in ripe bananas the sugar content is over 20 per cent.

Figs are one of the oldest known foods. They are high in carbohydrates and low in proteins and hence an excellent food for heat
and energy. The variety now extensively grown in California is the
Smyrna fig. Dried figs have a higher protein content than fresh
figs and contain malic acid, as do apples. Imported cured figs must
be closely inspected for worms and their excreta due to careless
selection and packing.

Oranges, grapefruit, lemons, and limes are closely related, but differ in the amount of their acidity and sugar. Oranges are the sweetest and have the least acid of the citrus group, and are regarded as one of the most wholesome fruits not only for sugar but for organic salts and organic acids. The rind is a valuable source of essential oils. Oranges have unusually long keeping qualities and it is possible to see trees bearing unpicked but palatable oranges from a previous crop side by side with a growing new crop. Trees can therefore be harvested continually for four or five months. This makes oranges an extremely stable article of commerce. Even after harvesting they keep well, making it possible to secure oranges in all seasons.

Pineapples are an excellent, delicious fruit. The flavor of Florida pineapples is more esteemed than that of tropical varieties. The natural sugar of pineapples is an excellent preservative in canning, but unfortunately canners sometimes add sugar—which is a mild form of adulteration.

The mineral content of fruits not only adds to edibility but to digestibility. Physiologically, lime and phosphoric acid are assimilated by the bones. Other mineral traces actively promote circulation of the blood and lymph, as well as osmotic pressure which facilitates passage of solutions through the membranes of the body.

Sugars and acids in fruits determine their palatability to a large extent, as one offsets the other for a distinct taste. Malic acid is predominant in apples, apricots, blackberries, cranberries, plums, pears, prunes, raspberries, and strawberries; tartaric acid in grapes; citric acid in oranges and its related fruits. A few fruits have no predominant acid but a combination of several. Among these are bananas, peaches, and pineapples.

> The principal adulteration in canned fruit is artificial coloring. There is, perhaps, no other form of adulteration which has so little excuse . . . The object of artificial coloring is to make all kinds and varieties of these fruits imitate those of a naturally rich color. Its sole purpose is deception since it can add nothing whatever to the nutritive value.

In addition to the above, the worst abomination Dr. Wiley described was production of maraschino cherries. This product is in all probability the epitome of all food fakery. First the cherry is bleached in a solution of brine and sulfurous acid until the natural color completely disappears. The cherries are then washed and the juice extracted, leaving little but a pulp as a residue. Then follows saturation with sugar, or sugar and glucose, and coloring a deep artificial red with a coal-tar dye or cochineal. Artificial flavor is added to replace the original flavor lost as a result of all the manipulating. The cherries are preserved in a solution of alcohol, flavored or unflavored, and then used in mixing cocktails or to decorate ice cream sundaes. The product is purely an artificial concoction, and as such is the ultimate in destroying a natural food and replacing it with an almost completely synthetic substance.

Canned fruits as a whole, if properly sterilized before canning, are a good and wholesome product unless saccharin is added. This is entirely unnecessary as the natural sugar in a fruit needs no supplementation. Since all additives should be mentioned on the label, the purchaser can make his selections with caution.

The fruit sirups for flavoring fountain drinks are a fairly important business commodity. Ordinarily fruit sirups will ferment after a few days. Few fountains prepare their own sirups and use them quickly but instead buy commercial preparations. To avoid fermentation, pasteurization is necessary which naturally adds to the cost.

The processors sometimes try to avoid pasteurization by using antiseptics such as salicylic and benzoic acids. In addition to this form of adulteration, natural fruit sirups are imitated by synthetic products. These are concoctions of the laboratory—weak copies of genuine fruit sirups—and undesirable from every standpoint.

The manufacture of jams, jellies, and preserves is also important in the fruit industry. Preserves are made from boiling the fleshy part of the fruit after treatment with a sirup; jams are the fruit pulp treated with sirup and boiled, while jellies are made from the fruit juice itself after treating with sugar and boiling.

Commercially it is of course possible to produce these products from inferior fruits. Boiling accomplishes two purposes—sterilization, and securing a uniform consistency by thoroughly saturating all portions with sugar or sugar sirup. The heating also prevents granulation of the sugar. It is necessary therefore to make jams, jellies, and preserves only from fruits that have just become ripe, as a product too ripe becomes less acid and cannot counteract sweetness. The more acid fruits are therefore more suitable for processing.

Jellies and jams are subjected to extensive adulteration. Artificial colors, artificial flavors, and glucose were often discovered by Dr. Wiley. In addition, he found salicylic acid, benzoic acid, or benzoate of soda preservatives. He also found that when glucose was not used, neither was artificial color or flavor—and when there was adulteration, all forms were practiced, proving that once a food is adulterated the practice is carried out to the limit. This was born out in Dr. Wiley's investigation of jams, jellies, preserves, and fruit butters as it was in other processed foods.

There is little chemical difference between the fats of animals and the oils of plants, both being combinations of fatty acids with glycerine. Oleic, stearic, and palmitic acids are the three fatty acids most important both chemically and nutritionally. When united with glycerin, the oils or fats are known as olein, stearin, and palmitin. The oils and fats are distinguished by their physical consistency at room temperature of about 70 to 80 degrees F.—the liquids being designated oils and the solids as fats. Both can gradually revert to oil or fat by the slow raising or lowering of the temperature.

Olein has the lowest melting point of the three, while pure stearin and palmitin can remain solid above room temperature and even above blood heat. Oils consequently have more olein in their composition, and fats, more stearin and palmitin. Animal fats are chiefly olein and stearin, while vegetable oils are principally olein; palm oil has a chiefly stearin and palmitin content.

Butterfat contains an important compound of fatty acid and glycerin known as butyrin, as well as small quantities of other glycerin components. Butyric acid is soluble in water; oleic, stearic, and palmitic acids are not.

Both edible vegetable oils and animal fats provide more heat and energy than any other foods. Measured in calories, one gram of edible oil has 9,300 in comparison to 4,000 of sugar or starch. Fats and oils are the most concentrated forms of heat and energy and from that standpoint are most valuable foods. They are also readily assimilated and have a favorable influence upon digestion. Edible vegetable oils are therefore very helpful toward correcting constipation or disturbances of the digestive process.

Edible oils are mostly used as bases for salad dressings and exercise both a nutritive and condimental effect. They can also be used as shortening in place of lard or other fats in bread and pastries, and in frying croquettes, oysters, and meats. Fried foods can be recommended only for the healthiest and most robust of stomachs.

In nearly all instances the seed of a plant contains the most oil; the only exception of importance being the olive in which the meaty portion around the seed contains the oil. The oil in other parts of vegetable plants is not sufficiently concentrated for good production. Proteins and carbohydrates are highest in the flesh of the roots or tubers.

The inedible oils—such as linseed, hempseed, and poppyseed—contain linoleic or some other acid which has a drying property rendering the oil too perishable for human consumption. Cottonseed, sesame, corn, and rapeseed oils all have some drying properties; olive and peanut oils have the least and are consequently more valuable nutritionally.

Cottonseed oil is one of the most important of the edible oils. Because of huge cotton crops in the United States, cottonseed oil refining has become a great industry. Refining for edible purposes requires highly specialized processing to eliminate impurities, distinctive taste, or objectionable color. Cottonseed oil is substituted for lard and similar cooking fats, and though excellent still falls short of being ideal or satisfying a taste for genuine olive oil—the ultimate in quality.

Olive oil has been the premier of vegetable oils since antiquity, and probably the first ever used in the human diet. In spite of numerous other vegetable oils cheaper and nutritively comparable to olive oil, its delicate flavor, excellent palatability, and high dietary value have preserved its position as the most desirable of all edible oils.

Because of its high price and close resemblance to other oils, olive oil is most extensively adulterated. Variations in tint among vegetable oils are no greater than variations among differing olive oils. Even a connoisseur of the most sensitive taste can be deceived when adulteration is limited to about one fourth of the total volume. Cottonseed oil—at only one-fifth the cost of olive oil—peanut, sesame seed, rapeseed, and poppyseed oils also have been often used as adulterants. In extreme cases, cottonseed oil has been substituted *in toto* and misbranded as olive oil. It requires delicate chemical and color tests to detect less flagrant adulterations.

The first pressing of the olive produces the best oil. The second pressing from the resulting pomace, after heating with hot water, is of a lower quality but still edible. Such oils are more suitable for lubrication or making soap.

Peanut oil contains arachidic acid which distinguishes it from other edible oils. The extraction method is similar to that of olives and the first pressing also supplies the finest quality of salad dressing oil. The cake left after the pressing is highly nutritious and contains some unexpressed oil, the protein matter of the peanut and other digestible elements. This is highly prized as fodder and also eaten as meal, but the excess protein somewhat unbalances it for human consumption.

Sesame oil approaches closest to the quality of olive oil and is consequently sometimes adulterated with cheaper oils. As a rule, only the best sesame oil is suitable for salads or making oleomargarine. The best variety is free from any unpleasant odor and has a light amber color. Sunflower oil is about equal in quality to sesame oil but is more extensively known in Europe than in the United States.

Cacao butter is an extremely pleasant tasting food which keeps well; it ferments and bleaches very slowly after long standing. Obtained by pressure from cacao beans, because of its high price cacao butter is sometimes adulterated with coconut fat and palm-nut fat.

Coconut oil or butter is obtained from the kernel of the coconut and solidifies at ordinary room temperature. It has a good taste and no unpleasant odor but rancidifies quickly, taking on a very unpleasant taste and odor in the process. Because of its low price, there is no extensive adulteration.

Palm oil or fat comes in many varieties and solidifies at about body temperature. Palm oil is a very pleasant tasting edible, with a fragrance reminiscent of violets. Often it is extracted in the crudest and most inefficient manner by natives and will be putrescent, water soaked or rancid. The dark, natural color is usually bleached; other adulteration is comparatively unknown.

Peanuts are probably the most widely consumed of all nuts in the United States. The production and uses of peanut oil have already been described. Peanut butter is processed by removing some of the stearin from the oil. It is as nutritious as the oil and its flavor is well regarded by those who like the taste of peanuts.

The other nuts are not particularly important as foods. Acorns were once utilized as pig fodder although such fodder produced a lard with a low melting point unsuitable for summer use. Almonds, chestnuts, beechnuts, Brazil nuts, butternuts, filberts, hazelnuts, walnuts, pistachios, and hickory nuts are fairly well known for their edibility and flavoring qualities. All are quite oily and fairly high in protein. Though an unbalanced form of food, nuts are nutritionally valuable and can produce a high amount of body heat. Nuts are an excellent food for those engaged in strenuous labor.

Mushrooms and truffle are the principle fungi used as foods. Their nutritional value is small, fungi being valued chiefly for flavor. Because of the dangers of poisonous fungi and the difficulties of distinguishing the harmless varieties, their use is greatly restricted.

CHAPTER XI

Sugar, Sirup, Candy

B ECAUSE OF his extensive researches in sugar, Dr. Wiley's discussion of the subject is particularly interesting. The principal sources of sugar are the beet in Europe and the cane stalk in the United States, where some quantities from sorghum, honey, and the maple tree are also derived. In Asia, the palm tree accounts for considerable sugar.

Sugar is an important commodity, particularly in the United States where consumption exceeds that of any other country. Many attribute our nutritional failings to an overconsumption of sugar. In 1886 Dr. Wiley wrote a remarkable paper on sugar which was extremely prophetic. He discussed the economic importance of sugar and advocated that the United States develop its own resources rather than depend upon imports. He warned of the drain on a nation's resources for sugar imports and that competition for the delicacy could lead to wars. In that paper Dr. Wiley predicted both the Spanish-American War, which was fought principally to insure our sugar supply in 1898, and the First World War, which eventually exploded in 1914.

In antiquity, honey was the only source of sweets. In the Middle Ages sugar cane was brought to Europe from Asia, and later to America. Louisiana became the greatest sugar producing section in the United States, but it could not compete with Cuba and Hawaii because sugar cane is highly susceptible to frost.

In 1747 a German chemist discovered beets as a source of sugar, but it was many years before commercial production was possible. Beets with a sugar content of 12 per cent—exceeding that of cane— have been developed in this country. In processing, the beets are sliced into thin ribbons, then enter a series of tanks for thorough treatment with hot water to extract practically all the sugar, which comes out jet black. Treatment with lime converts this substance into a carbonate with light amber tint. Filtering further lightens the color and removes the carbonate of lime and other impurities. Processing in vacuum pans evaporates the juice into a sirup with a distinctive color. Bleaching is done with sulfur fumes or by passing the sirup through the bone-black. Crystallizing the sirup by passing it through a vacuum strike pan and breaking up the crystals while they are still warm is the final process.

Cane sugar is produced primarily by grinding with extremely powerful mills. The juice is clarified with sulfur fumes, with lime also added to neutralize acidity and help coagulate the dissolved matter. The limed juice is then heated and at the boiling point a separation takes place, much like cream and milk. The clear juice is then drawn off. Further treatment is exactly the same as with beet sugar.

Maple sugar or sirup is a natural product if genuine. When maple sap is running, it is drawn off and evaporated. This is the only processing and the crystallized residue is the final form of maple sugar. Further refining would destroy its inimitable taste and flavor.

Refining is imperative with beet sugar, whose natural flavor and odor are disagreeable. Cane sugar, however, resembles maple sugar, for in the raw state it is far more fragrant and palatable than in the refined. Granulated sugar produced by refining is almost chemically pure, often approaching 99.9 per cent of purity. Such high concentrations were the nutritional overbalances Dr. Wiley considered dangerous.

The molasses remaining after refining is reboiled to obtain more sugar. When a white sugar can no longer be produced, the final and lowest grade is a brown sugar, sold for mixing with glucose as table sirup.

In refining, it is also customary to wash the crystals in the centrifugal with ultramarine blue suspended in water. This neutralizes the yellow tint in the sugar and creates the dead white appearance considered commercially desirable. Such sugar is inferior to the natural white of the first crystallization and is obviously a mass production device to reduce all sugar to one uniform quality far below that of the best. In concluding his discusion of sugar, Dr. Wiley wrote:

> While the refining of sugar can probably never be abolished, it should not be forgotten that the very finest sugar from a palatable point of view is that made from the maple or sugar cane without refining in which the crystals retain their natural yellow color. If consumers understood thoroughly the value of a sugar of this kind they would demand it instead of the dead white product which is now in vogue. A raw sugar of this kind could not be used if made from beets.

Adulteration of sugar is inherent in the manufacture which refines it too highly and utilizes deleterious sulfur and ultramarine blue for bleaching. Nutritionally, sugar is a valuable food, ranking next to oil and fat for producing body heat and energy. It acts quickly to relieve exhaustion and is consequently favored by those engaged in strenuous physical activities.

In general the remarks applicable to sugar also apply to sirups. Maple sirup is best when freshest and must be tightly sealed to preserve flavor. Cane sirup is delicious but unfortunately is bleached with sulfur fumes. An informed consumer would prefer a darker color as insurance against such adulteration. Experiments performed in the Bureau of Chemistry proved that sulfur or lime was entirely unnecessary and only detracted from the product. The same facts apply to sorghum sirup.

The original New Orleans molasses was a delicious product of old-fashioned kettle-pan sugar making. Crystallized sugar was placed in hogsheads with perforated bottoms to allow escape of the liquid matter. This separation brought a product of exquisite taste—the only kind of molasses known before 1861. Today its production is a lost art and "New Orleans" molasses is an entirely different commodity.

The vacuum pan and centrifugal processes in sugar manufacture have radically altered the character of molasses which is now decidedly inferior residue because much larger amounts of sugar are extracted from cane by modern methods. Consequently the proportion of impurities is higher in molasses, and since three different crystallizations are squeezed out the residue could hardly have much quality.

Commercial sirups are mixtures of two or more sweet substances. Glucose is usually the base as it is colorless and forms an ideal pouring body. Sufficient maple or cane sirup is added to the glucose to give a suitable taste and flavor.

Such mixed sirups are not objectionable as long as there is enough maple, cane, or sorghum sirup included to make the product appetizing. Molasses of good quality used in mixing sirups is not objectionable.

Adulterations are principally in the processes of manufacture—the sulfur used to bleach the glucose and sugar settling in the molasses used for coloring and flavoring. The same is true of lime, though it is not injurious in moderate amounts. Other chemicals which may be present are salts of tin used in washing, bluing, and the acid phosphates employed in clarifying the cane juices. The final adulteration is bleaching the molasses already containing the above substances by adding zinc and acid producing nascent hydrogen. Dr. Wiley consequently suggested molasses be completely abandoned for human consumption and utilized only as a good source of industrial alcohol.

Candy is in the same unenviable category as pastries and cakes, considering the opoprtunities for adulteration. The principal ingredient only rarely is an unrefined maple, cane or sorghum sugar. Usually the sugar is already highly adulterated through the process of refining—particularly if glucose has been included. In addition, starch may be used as a filler. Flavors, unless natural, are also distinctly undesirable as they are synthetic concoctions designed to simulate natural flavors of fruits, nuts, or flowers. Mineral coloring substances—even aniline dyes—are also added, as can be distilled liquors in rum candies and other fanciful creations.

In general, unless candy is made of old-fashioned but wholesome products, it further adulterates an already adulterated product, and therefore reaches about the acme of adulteration.

Honey is a form of sugar, different from all other because it derives from the bee's digestion. For centuries, honey was the only sugar man knew and it still may be the best of all sweets because of its exquisite taste and aroma and its sublime origin in the nectar of flowers. Comb honey is believed far superior to clarified varieties produced by heat with its consequent injury to the product.

Unfortunately honey can be readily adulterated. The temptation is great because of the high price. Glucose is an ideal substance for this purpose although its presence can be easily detected. More difficult to detect is adulteration with inverted sugar, obtained from cane sugar by the action of a dilute acid. This converts the sugar into a mixture of levulose and dextrose—also the constituents of honey. While such a substitution can be established by careful chemical tests, there is always a margin of doubt which can never be entirely resolved. A small quantity of cane sugar can also be added to honey and unless it completely changes optical properties, could well be overlooked.

The last part of Dr. Wiley's work on foods was devoted to "Simple Methods for Detecting Food Adulterations." The subject had also been treated in *Bulletin No. 100* of the Bureau of Chemistry by Dr. W. D. Bigelow, Dr. Wiley's very able assistant, and Burton J. Howard.

Among the methods of detection explained were those of distinguishing between such chemical and condimental preservatives as boric acid, benzoic acid, saccharin, and salicylic acid, as well as artificial coloring with copper, caramel, and tumeric. Aniline dyes were not discussed. A test for practically every method of adulteration or mixing was mentioned with easily procurable chemical reagents and materials. This material is so invaluable in the study of nutrition and dietetics that it should be included in the chemistry curriculum of every school.

The simplest test was on how to distinguish genuine butter from either the renovated variety or oleo. It consisted of merely bringing a small sample to boil, while stirring thoroughly and vigorously. Oleo or renovated butter will sputter noisily and produce very little or no foam. Genuine butter boils quietly and produces abundant foam.

CHAPTER XII

Beverages

THE COMPANION volume to *Foods and Their Adulteration* was *Beverages and Their Adulteration,* published in 1919 without further editions. This work too is a valuable portion of the legacy Dr. Wiley has left to us. It is both practical and scholarly and discusses the important properties of practically every beverage consumed by man.

Beverages are considered as foods and come under the provisions of the Pure Food and Drug Act. There are two broad classes— those imbibed primarily for their pleasurable, condimental, or stimulating effect and those which have a definite food value. In the former class are tea, coffee, soft drinks, and liquors; in the latter class are water, fruit juices, cocoa, and chocolate. It is hard to maintain a hard and fast dividing line, as some fruit juices are consumed for their pleasant taste while some alcoholic beverages, such as beer and wine, have been proven to have a definite nutritive value if made from proper ingredients and aged in accordance with time-honored principles.

Water is the most important of all beverages, absolutely essential to life and present in all foods. Every cell of our bodies requires water and in a state of thirst there is no better quencher than cool, clear water.

Water takes on the chemical properties of the soil and rocks through which it filters. The absorption of a sufficient amount of mineral matter to give water a distinct taste and quality classifies it as mineral water. These contain a wide variety of substances, some of which can be toxic. Because of excess mineral content, Dr. Wiley recommended mineral waters only for occasional use.

A water with a predominately iron content is termed "chalybeate" and valued for its tonic and curative properties. Sulfur waters are easily detected by their distinctive smell and taste. Where there are heavy deposits of sulfate of aluminum, the water will have styptic properties. Mineral waters are classified according to their remedial uses and not for nutritional properties.

From a hygienic rather than chemical standpoint, pure water is free from infectious or toxic properties. It is natural water which has filtered through rock and soil, uncontaminated by bacteria from sewage or other forms of pollution. In our modern cities it is necessary either to filter water or treat it with chlorine to ensure purity.

Technically speaking, chlorine is an adulterant but it is highly necessary to destroy bacteria. Chlorine also tends to destroy valuable nutritional elements in the system. An overdosage can be harmful. Some cities go to great expense to filter out chlorine through charcoal. Milwaukee paid $15,000,000 for such an installation in 1925. Fortunately chlorine readily boils and evaporates from drinking water.

Mineral waters have made such resorts as Hot Springs, Arkansas; Excelsior Springs, Missouri; Saratoga, New York, and French Lick, Indiana internationally famous. Their waters are bottled by local firms and sold under brand names. Misbranding is sometimes perpetrated by assuming foreign names, suc has "Vichy Water," which could only originate in France. This practice Dr. Wiley decried as a violation of both the spirit and letter of the Pure Food and Drug Act.

Another form of misbranding was to claim therapeutic virtues because of some supposedly valuable content of the water. Lithia waters as remedies for rheumatism and gout have been exposed as fraudulent. The quantities of lithia in some such waters were proved to be too minute to exert any therapeutic effect whatever.

Carbon dioxide to produce effervescence is another form of adulteration. The practice itself of carbonating waters is not harmful and carbonated waters have their place. However, it is entirely misleading to label waters as a natural effervescent type when it requires introducing an artificial process. This practice has evolved into a huge industry for bottling carbonated waters.

An imitation water cannot have the same medicinal properties as a natural water because of minute mineral elements, which can escape the keenest examination, and special properties impossible to duplicate artificially. Artificial waters made with proper methods of distillation, uniform in composition, sterile, and competently produced are unobjectionable as long as they are not labeled as natural waters or a false impression of medicinal value is not claimed. However, in Dr. Wiley's words:

> Mineral waters are not intended at all as a general beverage to be used every day; they are only to be taken at intervals and the longer the intervals the better. It is not a normal condition of affairs to be pouring into the alimentary canal a lot of foreign material which is not indicated in a state of perfect health. The value of a remedy is very greatly enhanced by its intermittent use and mineral waters are no exception to this rule.

Soft drinks are a gigantic business in the United States—more so than in any other land. Such beverages are carbonated waters mixed with sirup containing flavoring matter. If the sirup it made of pure sugar and such natural flavoring material as vegetable juice or extract of vanilla, orange, coffee, raspberry, strawberry, chocolate, etc., no objection can be offered. Unfortunately, too often harmful ingredients are included and the term "soft drink" becomes a misnomer. It is also inadvisable to drink cold liquids in extremely hot weather because of the sudden chilling of the alimentary canal caused. A slow sipping would obviate such ill effects.

Another objection in the summer is the high quantity of sugar in soft drinks, and Dr. Wiley advised:

> Sweetened water has very little, if any, value as a remedy for thirst. In fact one of the best ways to induce thirst is to eat large quantities of sugar or drink large quantities of sweetened water. Nature requires a lot of dilution in order to make this excess of sweets tolerable. Therefore there is little if any benefit as far as quenching thirst from the consumption of these articles.

Some soft drinks are decidedly habit forming, not only from the sugar but because of caffein, theobromin and even minute amounts of cocaine possibly present. Parents who would not serve their children tea and coffee at home unwittingly permit them caffein by sanctioning cola drinks.

Soft drinks are usually flavored synthetically and the same objections against such flavors in our foods also apply to beverages. There is no valid reason for synthetic flavors, Dr. Wiley believed, because natural flavors are abundant. Another hazard is storing soda waters in tanks lined with zinc or lead and the consequent possible absorption of traces of these minerals. Two most common drinks which deserve no place in the dietary are synthetic lemonade and orangeade. Both usually consist of only citric acid which has been artificially colored yellow.

The only objections to gingerale could be either using excess amounts of capsicum as a flavor, instead of natural ginger, or too much sugar. The same is true of pop, although the dangers from synthetic colors and flavors are also enhanced. Root beer hazards fermentation and the production of alcohol. Though the amount can never be great, even a slight amount is inadvisable for children.

Orangeade, limeade, and lemonade are all excellent drinks if prepared at home from natural ingredients. Commercially, the temptation is too great to use artificial colors and synthetic ingredients.

Cola drinks are noted for high caffein content. Coca-Cola once contained cocaine as a component of the extract expressed from coca leaves for flavoring. As a result of a long and bitterly fought law suit against the Coca-Cola Company about which Dr. Wiley made some interesting comments in his *History of a Crime,* the company agreed to use leaves from which cocaine had been thoroughly extracted.

Caffein is produced commercially from tea sweepings or extracted from various coffees sold as caffein-free. It is soluble in water and united with acids to form salts. Its effects as a stimulant are well known; very small amounts cause insomnia in some people. There are about one or two grains in a drink of Coca-Cola, tea, or coffee. Coca-Cola, as disclosed in the lawsuit mentioned, consists of about one third water, one half sugar, and the remainder caffein, phosphoric acid, alcohol, caramel, glycerin, lime juice, and essential oils in minute but definite amounts.

The benefits or harm of caffein have been discussed voluminously by experts, with wide variance of opinion. When such disagreement exists, Dr. Wiley was always of the opinion that a substance should be avoided for safety's sake. As a medicine, caffein has been found valuable but extremely difficult to control, bringing infections when introduced hypodermically. It also powerfully excites the brain and excess dosages can cause maniacal delirium, especially in the aged.

Cider is an excellent drink when made of good materials. Unfortunately, imperfect and inferior apples are often used. In warm weather, fermentation sets in within 24 hours to change cider from a soft to a "hard" drink.

During his career in the Chemistry Bureau, Dr. Wiley worked extensively on methods to prevent fermentation. One was perfected which proved commercially feasible. This consisted of using a clarifier, similar to a cream separator with centrifugal action which deposited solid or gummy substances on the wall of the contrivance and extracted a limpid, brilliant liquid containing no yeast. The cider was then sterilized by heating to about 145 degrees F. and then drawn off into sterilized barrels. Such cider would keep for several months after which fermentation and hardening would set in.

Adulteration of cider is accomplished first by using inferior apples. Benzoate of soda—which the method Dr. Wiley discovered to produce cider rendered unnecessary—is often added as a preservative. Sulfur fumes are probably no longer used.

Grape juice is usually a pure product, prepared without the addition of glucose, saccharin, salicylic acid, or other objectionable chemicals. The addition of sugar, to sweeten inferior grapes, or dilution with water are about the only methods of adulteration.

Coffee has no discernible food value. Caffein is of course present and consequently coffee should be regarded as a stimulant. Adulteration is sometimes practiced by adding chicory although, when properly labeled, chicory is not objectionable, as it gives a blacker color and adds body. Misbranding of coffee by misrepresenting country of origin can be practiced.

Tea was the subject of the first laws restricting food adulteration. Adding heavy materials, to increase weight, as well as adding spent leaves were old dodges. Sometimes leaves of other plants were added but this fraud is easy to detect as no other leaves resemble tea very closely.

Cocoa is highly recommended as a coffee substitute; it has a real food value. Fifty per cent of cocoa is fat. It also contains protein, caffein, and theobromine in small amounts. Starch and sugar comprise 20 to 25 per cent of the cocoa bean. The fat in cocoa provides heat and energy; its starch, protein, and sugar are highly digestible and as a whole nutritionally good. Its theobromine is less stimulating than caffein, to which it is chemically related, and therefore less objectionable.

Wine is an extensive subject. Those who wish to delve into it thoroughly will find Dr. Wiley's material in *Beverages and Their Adulteration* fascinating reading. He described the production of wine in all countries and supplied a history of the greatest vineyards, their production, and listed their greatest wine years. This section would delight a wine connoisseur for its erudition and practical information.

Dr. Wiley maintained that certain areas of the United States could produce wines almost as good as the best of other countries. In these regions the soils had evidently improved with age or possibly with proper cultivation. Excellent though our grapes can be he believed them to be not quite as good as European varieties—due to our virgin soils in most areas. The greatest factor contributing to the superiority of foreign wines, however, is the skill and care developed through centuries of practice in their traditional manufacture.

American wines have a poor reputation because of the extensive adulteration and debasement practiced—considered sacrilegious in old wine-producing countries. The most common adulteration is adding sugar because of a peculiar belief among grape growers that wine cannot be made without it. Water, too, is added and of these practices Dr. Wiley observed:

> When once the wine grower begins to add sugar or water to his grape juice the temptation to increase the volume of his product is so great that he does not know exactly where to stop. The result is that in many localities American wines are only partly made from the juice of grapes while sometimes as much as a third or even a half of their alcoholic content comes from totally foreign substances.

This is inexcusable as excellent wines are made in foreign countries with only a 6 or 7 per cent alcoholic content. Every 2 per cent of sugar added results in 1 per cent alcoholic increase. Wine is further debased by subjecting either the pomace, after one expression of the grape juice, or the finished wine to additional quantities of sugar and water. Production is increased by a second period of fermentation which can only be inferior in quality. Additives such as dextrose, saccharin, artificial coloring matters, and tannin have also been discovered in our domestic wines.

The chief obstacle to producing distinct and individual American wines is the foolish custom of labeling domestic products with names of foreign wine-producing regions, such as Rhine, Moselle, Burgundy, etc. All chance of developing a distinctive product is therefore lost as grapes differ in acidity, sugar content, flavor, aroma, and character according to the soil in which they are grown.

The greatest abomination in Dr. Wiley's belief was the production of "fortified wines." These contain added sugar and alcohol supposedly derived from grapes. Instead, alcohols from varying sources such as molasses or potatoes may be added. This travesty is actually encouraged legally and a fortified wine becomes a further adulteration of an already adulterated wine. Dr. Wiley described the product and the perversion of the law which permitted it:

> The fortified wine made in this country, or the fortified sweet wine is a beverage which must be looked upon with the gravest suspicion and the less used, the better. These provisos open the flood gates for legalized adulteration. There is little left for the professional adulterator to desire. The whole purpose and aim of the Pure Food Law insofar as purity of wine is concerned is set aside and denied. Almost everything needed for adulteration is specifically provided for by this Act. To be sure only 35 per cent adulteration is permitted. But who shall supervise and restrict the mad scramble to make adulterated wines?

The superfluity of the use of sulfur in making wine, or in treating wine barrels, has already been mentioned.

Beer, ale, porter, and stout are made from barley by converting the starch into sugar, mixing with extract of hops, fermenting with yeast, and aging in casks. Differences in the various products are due to slightly varying conditions of fermentation. In most respects, however, they are essentially the same.

The best beers are made only of barley malt and hops. Substitutions are unmalted barley, the starchy parts of Indian corn known as hominy grits, rice, brewers' sugars made by treating of cornstarch with an acid, and low grade cane sugars. Beer concocted from substitutes for barley malt and hops is of course inferior.

Another factor which determines the quality of beer is aging. "Lager" beers are those kept in cellars for a considerable time. Most beers today are aged quickly with agene to conserve on storage costs and bring them to market as soon as possible. In addition, bottled beers are pasteurized so that they will keep longer without injurious fermentation. Draft beer, drawn directly from the barrel as it comes from the brewery, is far superior to bottled beer.

Preservatives are not extensively used in beers, but they are legally permitted—as are fumes of burning sulfur. As both of these practices are unnecessary, domestic manufacturers of beer do not as a rule employ them.

Adulterations of beers are among the oldest known and ancient treatises have been devoted to the subject. The following is an excerpt from an Act of Parliament, passed over a century ago;

> . . . prohibiting any material or preparation other than unground brown malt for darkening the color of worts or beer, or any molasses, honey, vitriol, quassia, cocculus indicus, grains of paradise, Guinea pepper or opium, or any extract or preparation of molasses, or any article or preparation to be used in worts or beer for or as a substitute for malt or hops. . . .

One of the most important phases of Dr. Wiley's career was spent combating the whiskey trust's forcing of unaged and adulterated whiskies upon the market. A proper whiskey requires aging in the wood for a number of years—four is considered the minimum and eight, ten, and even sixteen years are regarded by connoisseurs as the proper period for securing a worth-while whiskey.

This would naturally put the cost of production far beyond the means of the average person and the whiskey industry consequently developed the practice of "rectifying." A small portion of genuine whiskey was mixed with pure alcohol, artificial flavor and coloring and sold as blended whiskey. This led to the bitter controversy which embroiled Dr. Wiley with the whiskey trust. Rectified whiskey drove real whiskey off the market. So great was the extent of this adulteration that it was estimated at the time of the passage of the Pure Food Law that 90 per cent of all the whiskey sold was doctored.

Adulteration of distilled liquors in all parts of the world has been continuous and extensive, with the United States leading the list. Brandy, rum, and gin are also adulterated in much the same fashion, of which the principal forms are:

1. Coloring of spirits to simulate aging—done with artificial colors such as caramel (burnt sugar). Storing whiskey in a highly heated warehouse, also bringing about simulated aging by a more rapid absorption of color from the barrel.

2. Diluting aged spirits with raw natural spirits made from any source which produces alcohol—in the United States, principally corn.

3. The least prevalent now because of the high revenues involved and the risk of fine or imprisonment—refilling bottles with either inferior grades or "moonshine" whiskey.

As the above adulterations also apply to brandy, gin, and rum, and the purpose of this work is to give only a general idea of the production, treatment, and sale of distilled liquors, further details are impractical. In general, present-day distilling practices—as in food processing—have worked to drive the most desirable and palatable forms of wines and liquors off the market. Most of the beers, wines, whiskies, brandies, gins, rums, and cordials consumed today are but poor imitations of genuine products—abominations not worth drinking. The delicate fragrance, aroma, and taste derived from the proper aging and production of distilled liquors from the finest ingredients cannot be faked, no matter how clever the alchemy employed. The best hope for the really particular and discerning consumer—as in the case of foods—would be to patronize only firms catering to a select and keenly appreciative market.

This concludes the discussion of the highlights in food adulteration as gleaned from Dr. Wiley's invaluable studies. No attempt has been made at a detailed and highly scientific discussion. The purpose is merely to give a practical idea of how our most commonly consumed foods and beverages may be processed and adulterated. The information has been presented purely for the benefit of non-professional readers and consumers to help them to a more careful selection and better nutritional return for their money, as well as ensuring more pleasing and appetizing taste.

CHAPTER XIII

Chemicals in Foods Today

For a third of a century the fight for pure food has been waged and the end is not yet. No great question is settled until it is settled right. The game is not over until one or the other of the contestants is checkmated. Draws do not count. During this third of a century it has been my fortune to be in the thick of the fight, at first as a private, then through the various grades of leadership to colonel or even general of the brigade, and now again in the ranks.

This battle has not, however, been a fight of a personal character as some late historians assert. It was and is a struggle for human rights as much as the Revolution or the Civil War. A battle for the privilege of going free of robbery and with a guaranty of health. It has been and is a fight for the individual right against the vested interest, of the man against the dollar.

AFTER THESE introductory words to *1001 Tests,* Dr. Wiley reviewed the well-known events leading to his resignation—the perversion of the Pure Food Law. Following his death, in 1930, other champions of safe foods continued the battle. Schlink and Kallett of *Consumer's Research* hammered away at abuses in their books, *100,000,000 Guinea Pigs* and *Eat, Drink and Be Wary,* which received widespread public attention. In 1933, Senator Royal S. Copeland of New York introduced a bill to amend the Pure Food and Drug Act, and after many changes and compromises it was passed in 1938.

109

In 1933 the Food and Drug Administration (FDA), which in 1927 had succeeded the Bureau of Chemistry as the enforcing agency, exhibited its "chamber of horrors." It displayed some of the rankest violations of public safety in the promotion of various drugs, cosmetics, and therapeutic devices the FDA had prosecuted. Among these exhibits were an eyelash dye that had caused blindness, hair dyes which had inflicted systemic poisoning, and all manner of worthless and dangerous elixirs, radium waters, and liniments.

Public opinion was violently aroused in 1937 when 105 persons died from imbibing an "elixir of sulfanilamide." This tragedy was reminiscent of the "embalmed beef" scandal of 1898 for the furor it aroused. The elixir was a concoction containing diethylene glycol as a solvent and marketed without bothering to test its toxicity. Before sales could be halted and the product seized, the mortality mounted to 105 with an undetermined number badly upset.

On June 25, 1938 the new pure food and drug law sponsored by Senator Copeland was passed. It was hailed as an advance and improvement over the 1906 law. Actually it was merely an acknowledgement that the old law had never been observed and had become a dead letter because of the emasculation Dr. Wiley described. The new law provided that any food, drug, therapeutic device, or cosmetic that was impure, dangerous, or misbranded could be seized and condemned. The law gave the FDA, which had been transferred from the authority of the Department of Agriculture to the Federal Security Agency, the power to establish reasonable definitions and standards of identity for foods. (It will be remembered that the Standards Committee, of which Dr. Wiley was a member, had performed this function very capably in the first decade of this century).

The joker in the new law was the lack of any requirement that manufacturers or processors need supply prior proof of the safety of a chemical before using it in foods. It was just this loophole in the law which had made it possible for the Elixir of Sulfanilamide to be marketed before its deadly properties were known. As is evident, some invisible hand always found a way to nullify the law or leave a gaping hole which permitted evading its provisions.

In other words, the law permitted any drug, chemical, or process to be used in foods until such time as the Food and Drug Administration became aware of its possible harm. When such evidence arose, procedure to confiscate the product and prosecute the distributors could be instituted. The burden of proof was therefore upon the government, whereas under the 1906 law the burden of proof had been upon the processor or manufacturer. This interpretation of the law had been upheld by the Supreme Court in 1914. A further joker lay in the fact that the FDA was hopelessly undermanned and operated on a miserly appropriation. Many gross violations could be continued for a long time before detection by the understaffed agency.

That was the *status quo* when, in 1950, Congress authorized hearings on "Chemicals in Food Products" under House Resolution Number 323. These hearings were continued in 1951 under House Resolution Number 74, and as subsequently published, comprise fascinating reading. Their proper appreciation requires orientation in the history of the law and the struggles of Dr. Wiley in establishing the truths about food manipulation and the insidious control of the administration by the very interests the law was intended to curb.

Reading between the lines, the record of these hearings supplies clues to further crimes committed after Dr. Wiley was forced from government service and the powerful interests he opposed became firmly entrenched in Washington. In the intervening years, many new products had come upon the market. The trend toward higher concentrations of population had increased, bringing with it increased problems in the storage, handling, and processing of food.

There had also come a highly intensified technique of selling and advertising; through radio and television millions can be reached and persuaded by clever artifices devised by experts in the art of presentation and misrepresentation. The chemical industry had become a powerful industrial enterprise, constantly creating new and more powerful substances to preserve, color, flavor, and spray upon foods. The pace had become greatly accelerated because of the rapidly rising population.

Through it all, however, the Food and Drug Administration had changed but little. It was engaged in a struggle become immensely more difficult and complex. The public, whose interests it was intended to protect, was blissfully unaware of what was going on.

Under the spell of scientific claims, all the new "advances" in food technology were accepted with hardly a murmur. At the same time, there was a growing awareness of the prevalence of cancer, heart disease, and other deteriorating illnesses which an alarmed segment of the medical and chemical professions was attributing to excessive use of additives in our foods.

The Congressional Committee was headed by Representative James J. Delaney of New York, well known for his conscientious interest in the subject and for his efforts to arouse the public to an awareness of the urgency of the problem. As a whole, members of the committee were competent and their questioning of expert witnesses called upon to testify was capably conducted. This was particularly true of A. L. Miller, M.D., former Health Commissioner, serving as Representative from Nebraska, whose medical background was valuable in clarifying the physiological and toxic effects of chemicals. Vincent A. Kleinfeld, chief counsel for the committee, is a well-known legal authority on food and drug legislation. Kleinfeld took an active hand in interrogating witnesses and his knowledge of the most recent developments in chemistry and food processing was impressive.

The roll of witnesses called was also impressive. They comprised outstanding authorities from practically every sphere, including physiology, biochemistry, endocrinology, internal medicine, pharmacology, nutrition, agriculture and animal husbandry, entomology, biology, and industrial chemistry. The government was represented by officials, chemists, and entomologists of the FDA. There were also chemists, executives, and research scientists from the baking, fruit packing, insecticide, chemical, pharmaceutical, meat packing, poultry, breakfast foods, and other industries. Representatives of minority groups, consumer cooperatives, and consumer research were also called as witnesses. Following is a partial list of the witnesses:

Dr. William A. Albrecht, University of Missouri
Dr. Firman E. Bear, Rutgers University
Dr. Morton S. Biskind, Internist, Westport, Connecticut
Dr. William B. Bradley, American Institute of Baking
Louis Bromfield, author and farmer
Dr. Charles S. Cameron, American Cancer Society
Dr. E. J. Cameron, National Cannery Association
Dr. Anton J. Carlson, University of Chicago

Dr. Faith Fenton, Cornell University
Dr. Robert S. Harris, Massachusetts Institute of Technology
Dr. Andrew C. Ivy, University of Illinois
Dr. Clive M. McCay, Cornell University
Dr. Francis E. Ray, University of Florida
Dr. Leonard A. Scheele, Public Health Service
Jerry Voorhis, Secretary, Cooperative League of the U.S.
Mrs. Leslie B. Wright, General Federation of Women's Clubs

About every viewpoint was heard—from the research scientist, soil chemist, and physician to the legal authority and farmer. Consequently the hearings comprise a unique and valuable compendium of current practices in the food and allied industries from every standpoint. The government published a total of 1,460 pages of testimony and practically every fact about food of any consequence whatever was recorded, together with arguments for and against more legislation and regulation of chemicals in food products.

It might be fitting to start with the testimony of Dr. John R. Matchett, whose position in the government could be considered comparable to that of Dr. Bigelow, who was Dr. Wiley's efficient chief assistant. Dr. Matchett testified on the "necessity for using chemical additives in processed foods, precautions to be taken in their use, and the economic consequences of their commercial application."

In the course of his testimony, which follows in part, Dr. Matchett summarized the extent of the use of additives and indirectly supplied a startling contrast between what is permitted and encouraged today and what Dr. Wiley strove to correct:

> The use of chemical additives in processed foods is as old as the art of food preservation itself. Fermentation, both alcoholic and lactic, has been well known since earliest times. Its use by man to implant in foods protective substances not originally present therein must have had its beginning in chance observation of nature in action. Then, probably a little later, the action of salt and smoke in stabilizing flesh foods became known. In more recent times we have found a host of substances effective in conserving or enhancing the color, flavor, texture, and nutritive content of processed foods, as well as for protecting them against microbiological spoilage. Without these additives, modern food technology could not keep pace with the increasing demands for food products of improved quality

and convenience in preparation for the table. As the population grows and living becomes more complex, the orderly marketing of agricultural products as well as the maintenance of our high dietary standards must depend increasingly on the use of processed foods of enhanced quality and stability.

One of the factors that profoundly affects the acceptability of food is color. Long ago we learned to characterize foods by their colors. Thus, margarine should be yellow, mint jelly green, and fruit desserts red, yellow, orange, purple, or green. This is accomplished for us through inclusion of harmless dyes in formulations where natural color of the food is insufficient. Regulations covering certification of each individual batch of certain coal-tar colors which are harmless and suitable for use in foods are provided for under the Federal Food, Drug, and Cosmetic Act of 1938. The historic background of the practice of listing and certification of coal-tar colors may be of interest. The original Federal Food and Drug Act of June 30, 1906 did not contain specific provisions in relation to it. As you know, it did enjoin against the addition of poisonous or other deleterious ingredients which might render food injurious to health.

On June 18, 1907 Food Inspection Decision 76, which listed seven permissible dyes, was promulgated. So seriously was protection of the public regarded that the Bureau of Chemistry (predecessor to the Food and Drug Administration) set up a program of testing each batch of the permitted dyes. A certificate was issued to cover each batch that met the required standards of purity. This procedure became known as certification and the particular dye so examined was called a certified color. No fees were collected for certification and compliance was voluntary by the food industry.

The present law continues the procedure of certification developed under the earlier statute, and places it upon a self-supporting basis. The present act, too, imposes upon the manufacturer the duty to utilize not only a dye upon the permitted list but also one from a batch which has been certified in accordance with the regulations.

Today, some 132 dyes, 18 of which are certifiable for use in foods, are enumerated in the regulations. Their manufacture and sale constitute a substantial industry. In 1947, the f.o.b. plant value of certified food colors amounted to $6,783,000.

Protection of natural color of products from deterioration in processing or during storage is achieved in some instances through additives. Many dried and frozen fruits could not be produced without them. You are all familiar with the brown color which soon appears on the exposed surface of apples, peaches, pears, apricots, and other fruits when they are cut or bitten. This discoloration is brought about by certain complex substances known as enzymes which are present naturally in the fruit. When the broken cells are exposed to air these enzymes enable oxygen to combine with specific constituents of the fruit tissue. The unattractive brown color results, accompanied by development of off-flavors. Treatment of fruit with sulfur dioxide controls the activity of the enzymes and prevents development of the undesirable changes. Without this control, dried apples, apricots, and peaches of acceptable quality could not be manufactured. The drying of these fruits is an important agricultural industry of the West which could not be carried on without the use of additives.

In packing certain frozen fruits—notably apples, apricots, and peaches—enzymatic discoloration poses a problem as serious as its counterpart in the dried-fruit industry. These and other fruits, unless properly treated, darken very rapidly upon thawing, since the freezing process has damaged cells and thus permitted the enzyme to act throughout just as it does at surfaces of fresh fruit. In packing frozen fruits, ascorbic acid (vitamin C) as well as sulfur dioxide is used frequently for control of this phenomenon. The packing of these products would not be feasible without additives and it is an industry which produced 77.6 million pounds in 1949. It may be appropriate to point out here that ascorbic acid would not be effective under the conditions which prevail when fruit is dried.

In commercial storage of dehydrated fruits and vegetables, especially at the elevated temperatures frequently encountered in military use, a second type of discoloration assumes an important role. It is caused by complex chemical reactions not dependent on the activity of enzymes nor the presence of air, but like the first it results in unattractive appearance and flavor. Sulfur dioxide or one of its salts inhibits this deterioration as well as that brought about by enzymes, and for this reason it is used in the manufacture of dehydrated vegetables as well as in dried fruits. In the latter case, it serves a dual purpose, controlling also enzymatic darkening as described above. One hundred

thirty-two million pounds of dehydrated potatoes alone
were produced in 1944, and though the industry has
languished meanwhile, it is possible that comparable
amounts may be necessary before the present emergency
[the Korean War] is disposed of.

The $14,000,000 maraschino-cherry industry is depend-
ent on another important property of sulfur dioxide.
Through its action the original color of the fruit is
bleached and the colorless product thus prepared is dyed
the familiar red by certified colors.

That lengthy excerpt, an accurate and faithful replica of Dr.
Matchett's testimony, reveals his viewpoint as sympathetic and
closely aligned to that of food processors. He also mentioned other
chemical substances believed effective in maintaining or enhancing
color but which had been dropped because proved unsafe. Thiourea, once used for preventing browning in fruits, was discovered
to affect thyroid function adversely and was abandoned.

Nitrogen trichloride was used to bleach flour for many years. In
1946, Dr. Mellanby of England reported it caused fits in dogs. Although, according to Dr. Matchett, nitrogen trichloride "had never
been found harmful to man" it was deemed advisable to prohibit
its use; such prohibition took effect August 1, 1948. "It is interesting to note that this action was taken at the instance of the
milling industry itself," Dr. Matchett said.

Processed foods, he also testified, demand many additives to
enhance or protect flavor. Among such sweetening agents were
P-4000 and Dulcin, eventually found unsafe; oil of anise, to give
licorice its characteristic taste, and vanillin, extensively used in
place of the principal flavorful constituent of vanilla extract in
commercial food production because of its low cost. Dr. Matchett
also testified:

The soft-drink industry, with a capital investment of
over half a billion dollars, uses enormous quantities of
flavoring materials. These include citric, lactic, phosphoric, tartaric, malic, and other acids which impart desired tartness to the product as well as complex mixtures
of odorous and flavorful components carefully blended to
simulate the flavor of a particular fruit. The artificial-
flavor industry in 1947 produced $16,500,000 in imitation
flavors, f.o.b. plant.

Dr. Matchett hopefully predicted that as a result of research done at the Department of Agriculture it would be found possible to separate the natural flavorful constituents of fruits, which some companies were already producing commercially for candies and soft drinks, to replace artificial flavors.

Antioxidants are used to prevent rancidity in fats—gum guaiac to protect lard and n-propyl gallate, butylated hydroxy anisole (BHA), nordihydroguaiaretic acid (NDGA), and dilauryl and distearyl ester of thiodipropionic acid are considered safe for use in edible fats and oils in concentrations carefully prescribed by the Bureau of Animal Industry. Other antioxidants were found unsatisfactory, according to Dr. Matchett, who further testified:

> Of special interest in the past few years is the rapid increase in the use of monosodium glutamate, made from wheat or from beet sugar processing residues. Having no flavor of its own, it accentuates many food flavors, especially that of meat. Monosodium glutamate is a salt of glutamic acid which is an amino acid, one of the building stones of proteins. In 1950 production of monosodium glutamate amounted to about 10 million pounds with a value of over $10,000,000.

To maintain texture, an "urgent problem of food technology" calling for retarding fat separation and settling solids in chocolate and chocolate-milk drinks, sodium alginate or starch is added as a stabilizer. Pectin is also put in jellies and preserves made from fruits deficient in that substance. Tribasic calcium phosphate is added to table salt to prevent caking. Alum is sometimes added to pickles as a hardening agent. The evaporated milk industry, products value $427,000,000, uses disodium phosphate or a similar additive for stability during processing and storage of milk.

To prevent ring neck, which is an accumulation of oily matter around the necks of soft-drink bottles, brominated olive oil is used. Calcium salts added to canned tomatoes maintain firmness and prevent unattractive mushing. According to Dr. Matchett:

> Firmness in the pack results in a greater proportion of high grade product, which means a higher return to the farmer and processor.

Emulsifying agents give desired smooth texture to salad dressings, ice cream, sherbets, and margarine and are used in the baking industry and for preparing mixes for home baking. Cakes containing emulsifiers do not fall during baking and bread maintains the texture of a fresh loaf for a longer period. Testimony also was:

> Over 45 per cent of all the cheese consumed in the United States is so-called processed cheese obtained by blending—with the aid of heat—cheeses of different flavors. The blend may contain seasoning, coloring matter, and emulsifiers, the latter usually consisting of sodium citrate or disodium phosphate. The processed-cheese industry is one of significance and in 1947 the f.o.b. plant value of its products amounted to nearly $235,000,000.

Dr. Matchett also reported that thiamine, riboflavin, iron, and calcium were permissible additives to flour—"to restore nutritives lost during milling." The enriching practice began as early as 1923 and in 1950 more than 68 per cent of all white flour produced and 80 per cent of all bread sold was enriched. Twenty-six states as well as the territories of Hawaii and Puerto Rico have made such enrichment compulsory.

Milk is fortified with vitamin D. Vitamin C sometimes is added to apple juice and frozen concentrated tomato juice and vitamin A to margarine. It was also testified:

> The addition of minute amounts of fluoride to public drinking-water supplies to decrease dental caries is becoming of increasing importance.

Since the Remsen Board concluded in 1909 that benzoates were "relatively harmless"—Dr. Matchett believed—it has found some use in cider, margarine, and certain other foods. Sulfur dioxide is used today in certain dry wines and fruit juices. Though these are permitted, he found other additives too dangerous after prolonged and careful experiments in his departments. One such was xylose, a sweetener found to cause cataract after continued ingestion.

Dr. Matchett mentioned the researches which the Department of Agriculture had carried out over many years to develop improved methods of utilizing agricultural products in foods, which is reminiscent of Dr. Wiley's original researches on sugar. When a new substance showed promise, thorough testing was completed and no recommendation was rendered without ample proof that its use would not be hazardous.

Along these lines, subtilin—an antibiotic to control microbiological spoilage in food products—was being extensively tested, Dr. Matchett reported. When the tests revealed that subtilin was of advantage in canned-food products in combination with heat, the results were publicized in scientific papers and the press to encourage others to engage in the same research. Beyond advising a long period of research to prove its harmlessness—as the tests of the Department of Agriculture are still not conclusive—subtilin was otherwise recommended.

In conclusion, Dr. Matchett maintained that the Department of Agriculture believed chemical additives were necessary if they enhanced quality, did not conceal inferiority, or the desired result could not be attained without them, and that it was necessary to continue thoroughly examining all the new additives being proposed and which would be proposed. This was an urgent responsibility the food industry and food research organization acknowledged, but only in the case of certain animal foods did there exist any government authority to:

> . . . examine the evidence of scientific testing, to conduct its own tests where necessary, and on the basis of findings to attest the safety of the proposed new chemical additives to foods before they are permitted to be used commercially. It is believed that there is need for the existence of such authority and that it might appropriately be met through amendment of the present Food, Drug, and Cosmetic Act.

This testimony supplies a thorough summary of current practices in the food industry from the government viewpoint. Some of the facts were decidedly ominous in spite of the very obvious intent of the witness to render assurance that precautions for the public's safety were adequate. Actually, the testimony could have been rendered by any member of the food industry or a spokesman for the Chamber of Commerce. There is little to distinguish the content from any of the advertising matter or the statements of the more commercially minded food spokesmen on the safety and value of their products. Very apparently Dr. Wiley's old Bureau had become nothing more or less than a subsidiary of the food industry —under its complete domination. There was something foreboding in the concluding statement that no agency existed authorized to check upon the researches of various food interests submitting data as to the safety and value of chemical additives—the very function Dr. Wiley had filled so capably.

At the conclusion of Dr. Matchett's testimony, Dr. Miller asked if there was some duplication between the activities of the Chemistry Bureau and the Food and Drug Administration which was under the authority of the Federal Security Administration. Dr. Matchett replied that his department conducted research toward improving the processing of agricultural products, while the FDA undertook to regulate processing practices for the protection of consumers. The FDA had no authority to pass on their researches, though Dr. Matchett said there was some unofficial contact to avoid any conflicts.

Questioning then proceeded:

> MR. KLEINFELD: Dr. Matchett, on page 4 of your statement you make the point, I believe,. that chemicals are often used to prevent discoloration in dried and frozen fruits during processing; is that correct sir?
>
> DR. MATCHETT: Yes sir.
>
> MR. KLEINFELD: In other words, there is a desire to use these chemicals in order to produce an attractive-looking product?
>
> DR. MATCHETT: Yes.
>
> MR. KLEINFELD: And that in turn leads to experimenting with various chemicals to find those which will, when used on the fruits, make them more attractive looking?
>
> DR. MATCHETT: Yes.
>
> MR. KLEINFELD: Now, when after such experimentation a chemical is found which seems to do the trick of, let's say, concealing the discoloration, is there not a tendency or at least a temptation to the packer, to use a chemical without worrying too much about how safe or unsafe it is?

This question was declared by the chairman as somewhat unanswerable as it would depend upon the conscience of the individual packer.

In the course of continuing his questioning, Kleinfeld elicited a very important fact, namely that the Chemical Department as represented by Dr. Matchett did not conduct any experiments on the toxicity of food additives, but was only concerned with

> . . . the improvement of utilization of agricultural commodities. You see, we have no specific authority or responsibility in the Bureau which I represent that is di-

rectly concerned with the toxicities of these materials. We would have use for them only in improving processing procedures with a view to improving utilization. And wherever there be occasion, we have not hesitated to use an additive material. We would certainly not advocate its commercial use, however, without full concurrence of the Food and Drug Administration in that.

However, further probing established the fact that there was no legal requirement for such consultation with the FDA and it was done purely informally.

Mr. Kleinfeld, chief counsel for the Committee, also was interested in the production of maraschino cherries by bleaching with sulfur dioxide and dyeing with a certified color. He was told it was done to get a more uniform color and a practice "that the trade has learned to accept." Kleinfeld then asked:

Is it a fact that sulfur dioxide bleaches out the dark pigmentation of rot spots in food, let us say in cherries, so that it cannot be determined from the color by looking at it that some part of the fruit may be rotten?

Dr. Matchett would not answer this question but Congressman Walt Horan, Committee member from the State of Washington, interceded with the statement that such practices would eventually become known in the industry and drive out those guilty of it, and while sulfur dioxide could cover up inferiorities in maraschino cherries it could not determine their ultimate quality and acceptability.

Sulfur dioxide, Dr. Matchett stated, was not regarded as deleterious. Mr. Kleinfeld then asked if it was not true that sulfur dioxide destroys vitamin B in fruit products. Dr. Matchett agreed that it did under certain conditions.

Kleinfeld also referred to the sweetening agents P-4000 and Dulcin—which Dr. Matchett had testified could not meet the high standards of the Chemistry Bureau for safety—to inquire if it was not true that Dulcin had been used for many years by diabetics and others who could not tolerate sugar. Dr. Matchett acknowledged it was true, yet his statement implied that their researches had resulted in barring the use of Dulcin before it had been used.

Mr. Kleinfeld also elicited the fact that lignin, derived from wood processing, was a component of synthetic vanillin. The witness

Courtesy of Assn. of Food and Drug Officials of the U.S.

DR. PAUL B. DUNBAR

could not say whether or not traces of lignin remained in the extract, nor if any comprehensive tests of its toxicity had ever been made.

This testimony has been quoted at great length because it originated from Dr. Wiley's old Bureau and reveals how completely his concepts and magnificent work had been nullified.

On September 14, 1950 Dr. Paul B. Dunbar, then Commissioner of the Food and Drug Administration, testified. He had begun his career in 1907 in the Bureau of Chemistry under Dr. Wiley and therefore in a way represented his former chief.

Dr. Dunbar's initial testimony was a review of the infamous Elixir of Sulfanilamide case which he called "one of the most tragic and hectic episodes" in the history of the FDA. Agents were dispatched all over the country to recall bottles in the hands of consumers. In some cases they succeeded in seizing them from medicine cabinets before anything happened; in others, death had already struck. As a result of the tragedy, Congress added a new drug section to the Act of 1938 making it compulsory for drug manufacturers to submit evidence of the safety of any new drug before it could be allowed in interstate traffic.

There was no comparable section passed in relation to additives in foods. It is only after a substance is added and the product so treated becomes a matter of interstate commerce that the Food and Drug Act authorizes investigation to determine whether a poisonous substance is present. Upon such determination, action may be seizure, criminal prosecution, or injunction, Dr. Dunbar testified.

He said that as a rule processors consulted with his department before adding any chemical to their products and tried to ascertain the best method of testing on laboratory animals. Such advice was freely given and this practice of consultation was therefore a valuable safeguard for the public.

He was asked about a salt substitute containing lithium chloride that had been offered in good faith for the use of individuals placed on a low salt diet. Dr. Dunbar said the danger of the product was unknown until continued use and consequent depletion of sodium chloride in the body had made lithium chloride extremely toxic. Action was then taken to remove the product from the market.

Dr. Dunbar also disclosed that mineral oil was a similar case of a product permitted until more adequate and thorough investigation revealed its harm. Qualified investigators working from 1941 to 1945 proved that mineral oil in the digestive tract interferes with the absorption of vitamin A, fat-soluble vitamins A and D, vitamin K, and other substances which would leave the user in a state of malnutrition. When used in pregnancy, it was also found to pre-dispose the newborn to hemorrhagic diseases. Infants to whom mineral oil was administered were sometimes afflicted with lipoid pneumonia. After long and hard-fought court actions, mineral oil was barred from use in any food product due to its proven injurious character.

Mr. Kleinfeld then questioned Dr. Dunbar about monochloracetic acid, the substance about which Dr. Matchett could not supply any information. Dr. Dunbar's testimony, however, was quite revealing. In 1941 the Food and Drug Administration had been requested to list monochloracetic acid as an acceptable food preservative. Experiments and studies by the Administration immediately established that the substance had

> . . . acute toxicity comparable to such recognized poisons as bichloride of mercury, which is otherwise known as corrosive sublimate, phenol, which is carbolic acid and strychnine. It had an acute toxicity one half of that of bichloride of mercury when administered to rats, one third when administered to mice, and one eighth when administered to guinea pigs; five times as toxic as phenol when administered to rats and showed comparable toxicity when used with other animals. We reached the conclusion and so announced that it must be regarded as a deleterious and poisonous substance which should not be permitted for use in food products.
>
> Subsequently, despite that announcement of its being our belief that it was violative of the statute, a great many products, particularly of the beverage type, were placed on the market containing monochloracetic acid.

Dr. Dunbar further testified that for three or four years monochloracetic acid was "a problem, a headache to the Food and Drug Administration." Recurrent episodes of digestive upsets, directly traceable to the use of the acid as a preservative in soft drinks, were continually reported. The manufacturer was fined $5,000 for the criminal offense of putting out a food containing an added poison—but before monochloracetic acid was finally banished from the market it had been used widely in a large variety of food products, such as salad dressings, pickles, wines, and soft drinks.

This case proved that even when the FDA was aware of the toxicity of a product manufacturers continued to use it, despite warnings, and years of intensive effort were required to keep it off the market.

Fortunately, in the case of thiourea the outcome was happier. Fruit processors took the precaution of consulting with the FDA on its proposed use for preventing mold on citrus fruits. Investigation disclosed it was highly poisonous and penetrated the skin of oranges. Thiourea was never adopted but the incident gives some idea of the scanty chemical knowledge of the citrus growers who evidently had succumbed to the sales pressure of some firm. One manufacturer of frozen peaches did use thiourea to halt enzyme activity and prevent darkening, and Dr. Dunbar testified:

> Fortunately we learned about it through a factory inspection almost simultaneously with the completion of the pack. We proceeded to take samples after the product had been shipped in interstate commerce and again we fed them to our experimental rats and again the rats expired overnight; we were able to apprehend all of that particular shipment.

Dr. Dunbar also commented that agene was first used about 1920 to age flour quickly. In 1947, Dr. Mellanby of England proved it caused fits in dogs; millers and processors then immediately investigated the matter. They confirmed Dr. Mellanby's findings and voluntarily agreed to discontinue using agene, substituting chlorine dioxide. Dr. Dunbar mentioned that he had always been suspicious of agene but had no definite evidence to institute legal action.

Dr. Dunbar also commented upon DDT, first used effectively in the Army and subsequently leading to the false impression it was harmless. DDT accumulates in body fat of animals after continued exposure to an injurious extent, Dr. Dunbar testified, which was particularly serious in cows. When the dairy industry was informed, it immediately instituted steps to use less objectionable insecticides and Dr. Dunbar further stated:

> Today our surveys of the milk supplies are reassuring. We seldom find, or find little, DDT in the milk supply, but it is something that might have developed into quite large

proportions had we not taken steps of the kind that I have just indicated.

The next subject was the "Condensed List—Chemicals In Foods," prepared at Dr. Dunbar's request in the Food and Drug Administration with co-operation of experts in the Public Health Service, to give a bird's-eye view to the Committee of chemical substances used in the past, proposed for use, or in current use in foods. There were about 850 chemicals on the list but the number in actual use was not disclosed.

Mr. Kleinfeld asked if the Food and Drug Administration had the function of defining and standardizing food products. Dr. Dunbar replied that such authority was vested in the Administrator of the Federal Security Agency. These standards pertain to the composition of food products and optional ingredients which may or may not be used by the manufacturer according to their proven safety.

In response to Kleinfeld's question as to whether the safety of a chemical must be proved in advance, Dr. Dunbar signified that such was the case. Unfortunately, this process of standardizing and certifying the harmlessness of an ingredient could not keep up with the speed of adopting new substances. As standardization was a slow process, many products were on the market that would not be standardized for years to come.

The same problem was prevalent in establishing tolerances in insecticides, about which Dr. Dunbar commented:

> One of the disturbing things about the recent advances in insecticides, in the discovery of new insecticides, has been that a great many very potent and valuable insecticides have been developed on which very little is known, either about their chronic or acute toxicity or about their fate after they are applied to food.
>
> In many cases we do not know whether the insecticide after application is absorbed into the body of the food, whether it is destroyed on weathering, whether it degenerates, perhaps into some more toxic substance. There were even insecticides put out for which no chemical method of analysis or identification is known.
>
> The tolerance-making authority is good as far as it goes, but it does not prevent the premature use of insecticides before their safety has been determined.

Of chemicals in general, Dr. Dunbar observed that they give a very definite improved quality to food, citing salt as an example. He also justified the use of calcium salts in canned tomatoes to make a firmer, more acceptable product. When asked about salicylic acid, Dr. Dunbar replied:

> Salicylic acid was held to be poison way back in Dr. Wiley's time at the very beginning of the enforcement of the Pure Food and Drug Act in 1906. It has been outlawed and has not been used in commercial canned foods . . . for at least 40 years.

Yet such requirements had been included in the original 1906 law which Dr. Wiley had been prevented from enforcing. Indirectly, Dr. Dunbar's testimony was a further recital of how that law had become subverted and he supplied another chapter to *The History of a Crime* which his former chief had written.

How far this retreat had progressed can be surmised from the following colloquy on May 15, 1951 between Dr. Charles S. Cameron, Medical and Scientific Director of the American Cancer Society, and Representative Horan of the committee:

> REP. HORAN: Now, supposing that the Administrator of the Food and Drug Administration, and it is his responsibility to keep anything that might be dangerous to mankind from interstate commerce—if you were the Administrator, where would you go for standards or procedures to determine whether or not any given product offered for sale should be denied shipment in interstate commerce?

Dr. Cameron replied, after a short "off the record" discussion, that he had been informed the FDA had laboratories physically adequate to conduct such tests.

> REP. HORAN: Frankly, I do not recognize the FDA laboratories as being in the same class as those of the National Cancer Institute or the Public Health Service. I just do not do it.

Dr. Cameron agreed to the extent that he could not imagine the FDA charged with the responsibility of providing information of that kind "at the outset." He suggested a number of other agencies, such as

> . . . appropriate subcommittees of the National Research Council; the Council on Pharmacy and Chemistry of the AMA; voluntary health agencies, and associations of food manufacturers such as the Nutrition Council."

Rep. Horan asked if these agencies were

> ... recognized by the FDA and if the FDA should accept their conclusions and "use their standards in their laboratories for testing whether or not to deny interstate commerce shipment?" In other words should they (the FDA) say, "We will follow this procedure here"? Has a way been found to validate these findings?

Dr. Cameron evaded the question by saying that involved getting into the philosophy of research, to which Mr. Horan replied:

> We are not getting so involved and I am not going to yield.
>
> DR. CAMERON: I am opposed to regimentation of scientific progress and opposed to an effort to reduce the accumulation of scientific facts to a channel and a method. I think that would be death to science and progress.
>
> REP. HORAN: I agree, but we are talking about whether or not this or that product should or should not be barred from interstate commerce. Now, do we have any agency that you know of that would meet with any degree of acceptance by the FDA, by the general public, or you?

Dr. Cameron replied that he thought the agencies he had enumerated, perhaps five or six of them, would be acceptable to him.

Congressman Horan persisted in his line of questioning to determine how the FDA would know whether or not a food was harmful, asking:

> By what agency are they given the standards by which they can arrive at that simple determination?

After more hemming and hawing, in which Dr. Cameron contradicted himself, he suggested that rather than depending on the agencies he had mentioned, such responsibility should rest with the FDA. He finally admitted, after being cornered, that there really was no scientific body qualified to make any final determination as to whether a food was harmless or harmful, and acknowledged:

> Those things, some way or another, have a way of swinging until everybody comes rather naturally to agree that this is the best way of doing things. It is a serious question whether you can force the issue by agreement.

One could well wonder whether the ghost of Dr. Wiley hovered over this curious, long-drawn-out colloquy which finally established the simple fact that there was no scientific body sponsored by a university, private funds, the food industry, the medical profession, or functioning for the government which could finally and definitely determine whether or not a chemical substance in foods had carcinogenic or other harmful properties. Surely the cautious and sane principle that Dr. Wiley had advocated so long and so earnestly, that where there was a shadow of doubt about a substance the doubt should be resolved in favor of the public by excluding it from foods, covered this situation adequately. In other words, if a substance could not be proved to have a beneficial effect, the absence of such proof indicated a strong possibility it could have a harmful effect; the less the positive value of a substance, the greater could be its negative and harmful components.

On January 3, 1951 the Committee reported on a number of substances used for years but withdrawn after discovery of harmful properties. Among them were:

Nitrogen trichloride (agene) already discussed in detail.

Paraphenetyl urea, a synthetic sweetening agent used as a sugar substitute for over 50 years by diabetics. In 1947 the FDA undertook a long-neglected toxicity study of continued reports of ingestion caused by the use of small amounts. Toxicity was quickly apparent and the product pronounced deleterious. One firm continued to sell it despite repeated warnings, as legal action could not be taken until the toxicity studies had been completed.

Lithium chloride, already mentioned, was on the market for about two years. Its toxicity after continued ingestion was also proved, but it was not withdrawn until several deaths had occurred.

Paraminoazobenzene or butter yellow, one of a number of certified aniline dyes, was discovered harmful and withdrawn from use.

To quote from *Consumer Reports*, September 1956, "Chemicals in Our Food Supply":

Since 1956 when the FDA began to apply modern methods of study and research to certifiable dyes, 15 food dyes have been re-examined for toxic, carcinogenic, or allergenic properties. Only one of these, Yellow No. 5 (used to color candies, icings, and pie fillings for example), has been conclusively shown to be harmless. Last year Orange No. 1, Orange No. 2, and Red No. 32 were decertified as too toxic for use in foods. The FDA announcement said that "while manufacturers will no longer label and sell these three colors for food use, they may label and sell them for external drugs and cosmetics, carbonated beverages, desserts, and such meat products as frankfurters; Orange No. 2 and Red No. 32 were used to color the outer skin of oranges and during the Christmas season last year some 150 children were made ill in California as a result of eating popcorn colored with Red No. 32."

The Florida Citrus Exchange, however, contested the ban against Red No. 32 on the grounds that it did not penetrate the skin of oranges—despite the fact that orange peels are used by housewives to make cake flavoring, marmalade, and other preparations. In June 1956, further commented *Consumer Reports,* a special committee of the National Academy of Sciences and the National Research Council reported that the FDA could not complete its studies of certified colors for 25 years because of lack of facilities and personnel, and was further handicapped by a lack of authority under the Food, Drug, and Cosmetic Law to specify levels of use.

Monochloracetic acid, as has been mentioned by Dr. Dunbar, could be banished from use only after great difficulty. According to the testimony of Dr. Franklin C. Bing, former secretary of the Council on Foods and Nutrition of the American Medical Association, even after its banishment a pharmacologist from a leading medical school, who had originally endorsed the product for use in a beverage, still insisted it was harmless. Other pharmacologists also still tried to persuade the Council to approve a product containing monochloracetic acid, despite the evidence against it.

Mineral oil, mentioned by Dr. Dunbar, had been in use for about sixty years before its harmful effects were discovered.

Monoglycerides and diglycerides, mixed with shortening to keep bread soft, were also mentioned in the report with the above chemicals without definite classification as harmful, though wide differences of opinion among experts over its safety were acknowledged.

Stilbestrol was placed in the same doubtful category, as were a number of pesticides whose danger not only to food consumers but to beneficial insects and bacteria far outweighed their possible value in destroying harmful insects and bacteria.

It might be advantageous if some of the investigators would follow the courageous example of Dr. Andrew C. Ivy, of the University of Illinois, in testing the value of a substance. During World War II, when Dr. Ivy was working with other scientists at the Naval Medical Research Institute on desalination of sea water, he testified that a salesman called to offer a small brick which he claimed would render sea water palatable. To determine if the ingredients of the brick were safe, Dr. Ivy proposed that they both go on a five-day fast and drink only sea water.

The salesman agreed and after a five-day test both were well dried out and their bodies highly alkalized. This convinced the salesman and his company that their product was unsuitable and it should not be made available to shipwrecked sailors. If we only had more scientists and salesmen of that caliber who would be willing to first try out questionable substances upon themselves!

That, however, had been a war situation. When Dr. Ivy was asked if he recommended that all substances be first thoroughly investigated by qualified research bodies before being ingested in foods, he replied:

> Exactly, because when I eat food, I don't want to be a guinea pig for testing food. I want the wholesomeness of the food to be thoroughly established before it is marketed.

Dr. Anton J. Carlson, the late renowned professor of physiology from the University of Chicago, also agreed that the burden of proof

> . . . should first fall on the industry, the food industry proposing to use them. But in addition to that, it seems to me that both government and universities—state governments, federal governments—have a responsibility at least to collaborate effectively with industry in establishing safety.

Dr. Carlson also testified that only experiments on a great number of different species could establish the safety of new chemical additives. He predicted that small degrees of injury in certain percentages of people could go undetected for generations. In commenting about the milling of wheat, Dr. Carlson observed:

> We throw away the wheat germ and the vitamins and a great deal of the valuable proteins and retain essentially the starch. We mill out or throw away 20 per cent of the good food. We do put back some of the iron, some of the

vitamin, and we call that bread or flour enriched when as a matter of fact it is still impoverished.

In an earlier session when asked to comment upon agene—which the milling industry had voluntarily discontinued because it was discovered to have caused epileptic fits in dogs, although no such effects on humans had been established—Dr. Carlson commented:

> That is not sufficient for me because there are many other types of nervous disturbances—hysterical, all types— that may be aggravated or introduced by this chemical.

A disease that had been traced to an emulsifying agent in vitamins—retrolential fibroplasia of babies born prematurely, resulting in blindness—was mentioned by Dr. Bing as an instance of new disorders which could arise through the use of new preparations. He testified that when the same vitamin without the emulsifying agent was given premature babies, the incidence of the disease went from 30 or 40 per cent blindness down to less than 1 per cent.

Dr. Theodore Koppanyi, pharmacologist and toxicologist from Georgetown University School of Medicine, questioned the assumption that foods long known in the dietary of man with no known untoward physiological effects could be considered wholesome;

> That is open to question. In fact, I would go even farther than that, and claim that historical human experience with food, even when these foods have been consumed for centuries, is not a completely satisfactory criterion because people often get sick and die of various chronic diseases such as arterial hypertension or malignant tumors and very little data are available to relate the consumption of even sample foodstuffs to human morbidity and longevity . . . The pharmacologist and toxicologist of today, however, is more concerned with the small and insidious toxic effects of substances that produce harmful effects when fed for months and years, even unto the second generation.

Returning to the subject of bread, the standpoint of the Millers National Federation was presented by vice-president Herman Fakler. When reminded that milling separated many valuable ingredients which as Dr. Carlson had said impoverished flour, Fakler contended:

> . . . Ultimately it comes back . . . through animals, poultry, and dairy products, in which the nutrients can be readily assimilated. Because of the rough character of the outer portions of the wheat berry, that is not digestible in

the human digestive system and therefore if the human eats it, it is actually lost.

When asked for proof of this statement, Mr. Fakler regretted he could not supply it at the moment. In discussing white flour, he told how unsatisfactory and difficult it was to bake with freshly ground flour and how baking qualities increased with the age and whiteness of the flour:

> It became quite evident to the flour-milling industry that flour and bread consumers were not only insisting upon optimum baking performance, but also were indicating a definite preference for a uniform white color in flour and bread. The industry recognized it had an obligation to meet this consumer preference and it devoted intensive thought, research, and experimentation to the solution.

Obviously the solution was commercially feasible and very profitable for the bakers because aged flour deleted the elements causing difficulties in baking, desirable though they were nutritionally. This made it possible to standardize flour and secure mass production. The "enrichment" policy was adopted to replace the lost natural vitamins, and Mr. Fakler said:

> It makes no difference whether these essential elements are supplied by synthetic products or are secured from natural sources.

After flour became so suitable for commercial baking, one more problem confronted the industry — the hardening of bread after staling. To meet that problem chemical agents to keep bread soft for longer periods were introduced. When a housewife doing her shopping squeezed the bread or "played a piano on it," as it was known in the trade, she rejected hard bread, which then became unsalable.

There was a wealth of testimony about Sta-Soft, Tween, Span, and Myrj 45, the polyoxyethylene monostearates adopted to keep bread soft. According to Dr. William B. Bradley, of the American Institute of Baking, his organization had not viewed these preparations with very great enthusiasm. To be sure they kept bread softer for a longer time, but they did not "inhibit staling." Softeners were of no advantage to the consumer and were also advocated as substitutes for shortening, Dr. Bradley said.

He recommended that the manufacturer should provide the guarantee of a chemical's safety and asserted that bread softeners were purely a competitive product which bakers had to adopt lest other bakers take away their trade. Louis E. Caster, president of a baking firm in Rockford, Illinois, also testified that he had adopted the use of bread softeners only as a competitive measure, believed it was of no nutritional value, and had discontinued its use when the question of toxicity arose.

In the hearings, the entire process of bread making was revealed— including the bleaching of flour, the milling out of nutritional elements difficult to control in baking, the enriching with synthetic vitamins, and the use of mold inhibitors, a chemical softener, and a wrapper impregnated with the smell of freshly baked bread. When the testimony had established all of that, Congressman Keefe from Wisconsin observed:

> The opportunity for a fraud being perpetrated upon the housewife is perfectly apparent.

An ardent proponent of the use of bread softeners was Dr. F. N. Peters, in charge of chemical research for the Quaker Oats Company. His favorable testimony was typical of the difference of opinion among experts as contrasted with Dr. Bradley's testimony and that of Dr. Roy C. Newton, research director for Swift & Company. Dr. Peters' firm was committed to the use of Span and Tween because they "did a better job" in cake mixtures than glycol products, Swift's emulsifiers, or those of Procter & Gamble. He said his mixtures were "foolproof." This was clarified by Representative Keefe as:

> . . . a cake mixture that the housewife can take and mix up in a batter, put it in her tray and put in the oven and bake so it will fluff up, look nice, not fall down in the center and stick out on the edges.

"Or stick to the pan," added Dr. Peters, who also said it was their aim to secure a cake that the housewife, judging from previous formulas, would call "a little better cake." Mr. Keefe then exclaimed, it can be assumed rather emphatically:

> Now, you are proceeding upon the sales psychology that you have adopted, well knowing that the average American has little or no interest in the nutritional value of the product that he or she takes into her mouth, has little or no interest in what may be in that product, but they have a

consuming interest in how it appeals to the sense of taste, and when these three esthetic things have been complied with you have a great product, and it may be the worst thing in the world for that person to eat from a nutritional standpoint.

Dr. Edward Eagle, a physiologist and toxicologist in the employ of Swift & Company, had tested the effects of Sta-Soft, Myrj 45, Tween, and Span on rats and hamsters. He testified that animals fed with those products suffered from diarrhea and marked inflammations around the anus. After sacrificing the animals, pathological examinations revealed many marked disturbances and alterations in organs and cells. This, it must be remembered, was testing carried out by a competitive organization with its own shortenings made of cottonseed oil, soybean oil, and lard. Proponents of bread softeners were naturally inclined to discredit research sponsored by competitors.

Dr. John C. Krantz Jr., professor of pharmacology at the University of Maryland School of Medicine, had conducted similar experiments with Span, Tween and Myrj products. Approximately 2,850 rats and 38 monkeys were used and nearly 2,200 microscopic sections of vital organs of the test animals were examined, with this conclusion:

> The results of these examinations were found to be within normal variations. In other words, there were revealed no microscopic abnormalities that could be attributed to the feeding of the emulsifiers.

Dr. Robert S. Harris, of the Massachusetts Institute of Technology Nutritional Biochemistry Laboratories, had also studied effects of the same emulsifiers. He reported at the bread hearings of the FDA in June 1948 that all of the emulsifiers had produced marked pathology. Most of the rats fed Span 20 died in a few days; the survivors developed bladder stones, kidney stones, fatty livers, and gangrenous tails. Tween 20 produced 57 per cent mortality, impaired growth, diarrhea, and poor food utilization. Myrj 45 produced similar results. Dr. Harris' study was not sponsored by a competitor.

Dr. Hedrick, a member of the committee, contributed interesting if informal evidence from his own experience:

A few days ago at my home, we were forced in by 30 inches of snow, and I was forced to feed chickens fresh bread that had softener in it. They all became sick. They developed dysentery and diarrhea after the use of this bread.

The same marked differences of opinion among experts were manifested in testimony on the use of stilbestrol for fattening poultry and cattle. Dr. Theodore C. Byerley, of the Bureau of Animal Industry, Department of Agriculture, testified that estrogenic elements were very common in nature and the hazard from ingesting small amounts of stilbestrol from eating poultry was negligible. It was ascertained that the attitude of the Department of Agriculture was somewhat favorable toward the use of stilbestrol, without giving any actual endorsement. In view of the fact that "there was no evidence of harm," Dr. Byerley felt there was no valid reason why the Department of Agriculture should prohibit the use of stilbestrol.

Disputing this opinion Dr. Robert K. Enders, professor of zoology at Swarthmore College, testified:

As research reports on diethylstilbestrol continue to appear the results are so conflicting that by careful selection and by inference from the results of selected experiments one can believe that it is either a blessing or a curse. . . . It is my belief that it is against the public interest to permit its use and sale under present conditions.

Dr. Enders based his opinion on experimental use of stilbestrol which had produced sterilization in mink. Mink breeders had sued the government for recommending chicken waste from implanted birds as suitable feed, because it was found to produce widespread sterility. Dr. Enders also cited the fact that extremely small doses of stilbestrol had sterilized laboratory animals where larger doses had no effect. He agreed with endocrinologists who contended that use of the hormone was an economic fraud:

Chicken feed is not saved; it is merely turned into fat instead of protein. Fat is abundant in the American diet so more is undesirable. . . . This fat is of very doubtful value and is in no way the dietary equal to the protein that the consumer thinks he is paying for.

Another danger Dr. Enders mentioned was imperfectly planted and imperfectly absorbed pellets leaving a high residue of stilbestrol in poultry.

Another strong opponent of the use of stilbestrol was Dr. Carl G. Hartman, of the Ortho Research Foundation, endowed by a pharmaceutical firm. Dr. Hartman presented a short discourse that was phenomenal for its packed, terse scientific data. His paper was divided into two parts—the over-all effects of estrogen and the economic aspects of its use. As to over-all effects:

> The liver and body fat stores more of the hormone than any other organ, as has been known for 20 years. . . . It is now axiomatic that estrogens, as well as other steroids, cause involution of testes and ovaries. They act chiefly by inhibiting the activity of the master gland. . . . Estrogens affect the pituitary, inhibiting all its functions . . . affect enzymes on which all bodily functions depend, inhibiting the important oxidases and dehydrogenases.

Obviously, then, there is distinct danger from estrogen intake, which Dr. Hartman said retained its high activity after becoming absorbed in the flesh of fowl. It was not only an extremely active substance when taken internally, but also when rubbed on the skin as a salve.

On the economic side, Dr. Hartman testified:

> So far as I know, it has not been demonstrated that small quantities of estrogen produce more flesh to eat or bone for soup . . . the fat of treated fowl differs chemically from that of normally fattened birds and it is watery and inferior culinarily. . . . The excess fat raises the cost of the flesh which has been purchased by the pound. . . . The flesh is said to be tender but less palatable than that of normal birds. . . . The skin is improved in looks, partly by the swollen and stimulated connective tissue underneath, partly by its more "female" texture. Hence such birds receive a fictitiously high rating for quality.

On the other hand, Dr. Robert B. Greenblatt, professor of endocrinology at the Medical College of Georgia, differed markedly from such opinions. He contended that estrogen was not stored in the tissues and was rapidly excreted in the urine and that any sterility from overdosage would only be temporary. He made no comments upon the quality of meat produced through stilbestrol feeding nor on its palatability, confining himself primarily to maintaining that harmful possibilities of stilbestrol in foods were exaggerated.

CHAPTER XIV

Fertilizers and Insecticides

THE FARM as well as the land itself is a food processing factory now that hormones, antibiotics, sprays, and fertilizers are so liberally used in meat and crop production. The Hearings devoted some time to a discussion of soils—their need for fertilizer, theories of the organic school as opposed to chemical fertilizers, and depletion of valuable elements in the soil through intensive agriculture.

Dr. William A. Albrecht, Chairman of the Department of Soils, University of Missouri, is well known for his work in soil conservation. His concept of crop production was based on quality:

> I am not so much concerned merely in bushels and tons but I am interested in whether feed and food have nutritional value of a complete order rather than fattening value, which is so easily produced on almost any soil. . . . The belief that chemical salts as fertilizers on the soil should result in plants which damage the health of man and animals on their consumption, is a matter of fancy and not of fact. It is the injudicious use of a fertilizer that is dangerous but not the judicious use of a fertilizer.

Plants, too, can look well and appear as if they were complete, but Dr. Albrecht testified he had grown beautiful soybeans which actually had less nitrogen, phosphorus, and potash than their seed, and these plants could not reproduce themselves.

A healthy plant is its own protection against insects, Dr. Albrecht believed. To illustrate, he mentioned an experiment in which four rows of spinach were planted with 5, 10, 20, and 40 units of nitrogen

138

fertilizer respectively. The first two rows were attacked by insects but the last two were not because their protein content was high. This would appear to bear out the contention of many soil nutritionists that a healthy plant will never become the victim of disease or insects and spraying is unnecessary as it does not correct the underlying cause—a poorly nourished plant.

Another fallacy Dr. Albrecht attacked was the contention that fertilizers ruin the soil. He maintained that a fertilizer balances the elements in the soil and consequently takes out these elements faster. Therefore they do not ruin the soil but cause it to wear out faster. Perhaps Dr. Albrecht's most interesting statement was one bearing on synthetic chemicals and their possible danger when applied to food and soils:

> As you start by administering near the soil and come up through the microbes and the plant and the animals and then to man, as his food, you have increased your safety factor because you have interposed a lot of natural performance between that chemical and your food or yourself. But when you impose chemicals near man's food directly and the last step of consuming that food, then your danger becomes greater. So when you bury anything in the soil and let it come through food from there, the microbes have worked it over, the plant has worked it over, the animal has worked it over and from then on, taking the animal products as food is much more safe because you have escaped the dangers.

From the standpoint of the consumer, this is probably the clearest and most lucid explanation of why natural food elements are so much more beneficial than synthetic elements, and why injurious elements that have gone through the complicated process mentioned lose their toxicity.

The capacity of plants to take up chemicals readily from the soil was attested by Professor Emil Truog, Chairman of the Department of Soils, University of Wisconsin, in testifying on the effect of applying fertilizers, the condition of soils after such application, and quantity and nutritive quality of crops grown on them. Dr. Truog emphatically asserted that soils properly fertilized will not be injured.

Though he disputed assertions of organic farmers that chemicals ruin the soil, he acknowledged that fertilizers which contain extraneous and toxic matter are harmful because plants readily absorb notable amounts of soluble substances, whether they need them for growth or not. He quoted selenium as an example and cited its fatal effects on cattle grazing on grasses absorbing the chemical.

It is therefore somewhat reassuring to learn that the consumer need not worry so much about the proper use of chemical fertilizers to produce his food. But crops which must depend on liberal and continued use of insecticides and sprays should be highly suspect as they originate in deficient soils, according to Dr. Albrecht, and also according to Dr. Truog by implication.

That using insecticides arises from a phobia somewhat like the excessive fear of microbes, was evident from the hearings. Fear of crop damages and losses has evidently been cleverly capitalized upon by manufacturers of insecticides, and their use is promulgated even by organizations of high scientific standing. In their brochure on "Use of Chemical Additives in Foods," the National Academy of Sciences published this statement on pesticides in 1951:

> Many crops would be destroyed if left unprotected. Heavy investments in land, fertilizer, expensive farm machinery, and labor must be protected from crop losses due to devastation by disease.

Dr. Leonard A. Scheele, U.S. Surgeon General, testified both on the advantages and dangers of pesticides. In destroying the bearers of malaria and typhus, he said there was an attendant danger of contaminating food. The problem of insecticides is apparently essentially the same as that of chemical additives in foods, raising a question as to which is the greater danger—eating a contaminated food or a food which contains a toxic substance used to prevent contamination.

The proper use of insecticides and the responsibility for safety against personal exposure to dangerous chemicals rests on the user, testified various pesticide manufacturers who also mentioned the notable step-up in the use of pesticides after World War II which brought adoption of DDT. The problem thereupon had become acute and the question of tolerances called for delicate chemical determinations of the amount of spray residue permissible on fruits and vegetables.

The view of forceful proponents of pesticides was represented by the secretary of the International Apple Association. He gave a somewhat curious twist to his argumentation by contending that the history of science shows many instances of views held persistently only to be refuted with the advance of scientific knowledge. He cited the case of golgi, a theory in relation to cells based on inaccurate observations through the microscope, later corrected by developing better microscopes and techniques. Therefore the witness contended that views on tolerances and restrictions in the use of insecticides, too, would be lifted as science progressed and proved insecticides were less dangerous than now believed.

The gentleman evidently was not aware of the fact that developments in technology had been just the opposite and led to reversal of opinions on the harmlessness of various chemicals such as agene, monochloracetic acid, and some aniline dyes and food preservatives. Advocates of insecticides insisted that more and more spraying became necessary because insects developed immunity to certain sprays, which had to be continually changed. They also acknowledged that many beneficial insects and birds were also killed by insecticides, but it was a "calculated risk."

The specter of famine and complete crop destruction was continually held up by these proponents. One witness mentioned spending several hours in an 80-acre orchard that had not been sprayed for three years. Of the thousands of bushels of apples on the trees or on the ground, he said he could not find one that would pass inspection in a commercial pack.

On the surface, this would appear like a very convincing argument for the use of sprays except for the possibility Dr. Albrecht had mentioned that properly nourished crops provide their own protection against parasites and disease. It is also known that insects such as the codling moth attack only overripe apples. An unattended orchard would necessarily contain such overripe fruit with the increased possibility of attack by worms and moths.

In recent years the biggest hazard has arisen from the use of DDT, which is being continually attacked as a highly dangerous and also ineffective insecticide once insects develop immunity. DDT has been proved to collect in the fatty tissue of animals producing milk and milk products. A startling confirmation of widespread prevalence of DDT residue was provided by John Dendy, head of the analytical chemistry division of the Texas Research Foundation. Mr.

Dendy was occupied with research on whether DDT contamination was extensive in milk and meats offered for sale, the degree of such contamination if it existed, whether plants were absorbing DDT after spraying and the extent if any. He summarized:

1. All processed milk and most samples were found to be contaminated with DDT.

2. The degree of contamination ranged from 3.10 parts per million of DDT in lean meat to 68.55 parts per million in fat meat. In milk the contamination ranged from less than 0.5 parts per million to 13.83.

3. Both corn and sunflowers sprayed with insecticides were found to absorb the chlorinated hydrocarbons in unchanged form.

4. The rate of absorption was found to be cumulative, the degree of contamination increasing with each spraying.

Based on these findings, the Texas Research Foundation concluded that existing laws were inadequate and that the continued indiscriminate use of DDT and other chlorine hydrocarbons held an ever-increasing hazard to public health.

Louis Bromfield, the late well-known author and farmer testified that he had found the use of insect sprays and DDT almost entirely unnecessary. He contended that proper land use and soil nutrition eliminated the necessity for insecticides, as did Dr. Albrecht, and that orchardists and vegetable growers of his acquaintance had eliminated the use of insecticides through proper cultivation.

Dr. Fred C. Bishopp, of the U.S. Bureau of Entomology, testified that DDT was an invaluable preventive of disease and had stopped epidemics of louse-borne typhus in heavily infested populations during World War II. He credited DDT with reducing the incidence of marine typhus in ten states by 80 per cent, reducing dysentery in children through fly control, making the bedbug a rarity, and reducing food contamination through cockroach and ant control—as well as saving millions of dollars in clothing, rugs, and other fabrics by destroying moths and carpet beetles. Not one death could be attributed to exposure to DDT. Dr. Bishopp's report was extremely favorable.

On the other hand, Dr. Morton S. Biskind, an internist with considerable experience in treating patients exposed to DDT, testified:

The introduction for uncontrolled general use by the public of the insecticide DDT or chlorophenothane and the series of even more deadly substances that followed, has had no previous counterpart in history. Beyond question, no other substance known to man was ever before developed so rapidly and spread indiscriminately over so large a portion of the earth in so short a time. This is the more surprising as, at the time DDT was released for public use, a large amount of data was already available in the medical literature showing that this agent was extremely toxic for many different species of animals, that it was cumulatively stored in the body fat and that it appeared in the milk. At this time a few cases of DDT poisoning in human beings had also been reported. These observations were almost completely ignored or misinterpreted.

Dr. Biskind supplemented his testimony with detailed case histories of many cases he diagnosed as DDT poisoning. The symptoms, which he described in great detail, included gastrointestinal upset, muscular weakness, disturbance of balance, headache, and nausea, becoming acute when patients lost weight and discharged DDT from dissolving fat into the blood stream. Cures and alleviations were effected by removing the patient from exposure to DDT.

Dr. Biskind's was a minority viewpoint. As the chairman of the committee pointed out in his cross-examination, in which he complimented Dr. Biskind highly, the great majority of opinion held DDT was valuable and harmless and the good greatly outweighed the bad.

A statement by the Federal Security Agency and the Department of Agriculture strongly endorsing DDT was read. The statement was issued following a meeting of representatives of practically every government agency connected with public health, including the office of the Surgeon General, the FDA, the Public Health Service, the Bureau of Medicine and Surgery of the Navy, Animal Industry, Dairy Industry, etc.

In the hearings, another authority of independent viewpoint similar to Dr. Biskind was Dr. Clive M. McCay, professor of nutrition, Cornell University. He reported on the many problems arising because of the use of chemical additives in foods and of the growing amount of his correspondence from laymen concerned with the effects of new chemicals constantly being introduced.

Since 1943 Dr. McCay had devoted substantial research to the injurious effects of cola drinks. During World War II Dr. McCay discovered that these drinks contained .055 per cent phosphoric acid, the same amount disclosed in the suit of 1911 which Dr. Wiley prosecuted.

Teeth placed in phosphoric acid softened and began to dissolve. In experiments carried out by Dr. McCay on rats given only cola to drink for six months, though well fed otherwise, their molar teeth dissolved down to the gum line. Monkeys suffered the same erosion. Dr. McCay published tables showing the rates at which human teeth dissolve when suspended in cola beverage and testified the drinks also had a bearing in gastric ulcer, because of their caffein content, and in the health and welfare of children.

Consumers were heard in the persons of Jerry Voorhis, executive secretary of the Cooperative League of the U.S.; F. J. Schlink, of *Consumer's Research* and co-author of *100,000,000 Guinea Pigs;* and Mrs. Leslie B. Wright, chairman of the department of legislation, General Federation of Women's Clubs. All urged passage of more effective legislation controlling the use of chemicals in foods.

Mr. Voorhis advocated legislation giving the FDA authority to certify in advance of use the safety of chemical ingredients in foods, insecticides, and fertilizers — to coincide with their authority on drugs. He also suggested that provisions for labeling requirements be stiffened to prevent misrepresentation.

Voorhis also mentioned how co-operatives were stimulating interest in Triple Rich bread, made from a formula created by Dr. McCay who proved rats could flourish on an exclusive diet of his bread but died on a ration of ordinary white bread. His formula called for 8 per cent milk solids, 2 per cent wheat germ, and 6 per cent soy flour—with chemicals or bleaches excluded.

The bread proved instantly popular even though costing two cents more than an ordinary white loaf. It was adopted by New York State mental institutions and consumed by 125,000 patients. Chain stores and co-operatives were enthusiastic buyers. The loaf was economical and a good source of vitamins and nutrients for those in moderate circumstances. A half-million families were buying and enjoying Triple Rich bread, which was somewhat interesting evidence of how quickly a palatable bread unadvertised and unpromoted can be welcomed by the public.

On June 30, 1952 the Select Committee to Investigate the Use of Chemicals in Foods and Cosmetics submitted its report, of which the following are excerpts:

The number of chemicals entering the food supply of the nation has increased tremendously in the last decade. Chemical substances are being introduced into the production, processing, storage, packaging, and distribution of food at an ever-increasing rate. Some eminent pharmacologists, toxicologists, physiologists, and nutritionists expressed the fear that many of the chemicals being added to food today have not been tested sufficiently to establish their nontoxicity and suitability for use in food. These scientists are not so much concerned with the acutely toxic compounds whose harmfulness can readily be detected, as with those chemicals which may produce harmful effects only after being ingested for months or perhaps years. . . .

The United States Food and Drug Administration in collaboration with the United States Public Health Service revealed that approximately 842 chemicals are used, have been used, or have been suggested for use in foods. Of this total, it was estimated that 704 are employed today and that of these 704 only 428 are definitely known to be safe. Thus, there are approximately 276 chemicals being used in food today the safety of which has not been established to the satisfaction of many groups concerned with the health and safety of the public.

The Surgeon General of the Public Health Service pointed out that the extent of this problem cannot be fully visualized because of a lack of adequate information on the chronic effects of chemical substances currently in use. He testified that the toxic effects of many of these chemicals and of the compounds which they form when introduced into food are unknown. He expressed concern over the possible adverse effects which chemicals used in food products may have upon human health.

The Committee reviewed some harmful chemicals used and later outlawed. These included nitrogen trichloride (agene), thiourea, paraphenetyl urea, lithium chloride, mineral oil, monochloracetic acid, and dehydroacetic acid, as has already been mentioned. In addition, the committee also reviewed the emulsifiers, the use of pesticides in general, and DDT, chlordane, selenium, phenylmercury compounds, and benzene hexachloride in particular. The report closed with this recommendation:

In conclusion, the evidence has convinced your Committee that chemicals have been utilized in and on the food supply of the nation without adequate and sufficient testing of their possible long-range injurious effects; that the public is entitled to greater protection with respect to the foods it must necessarily consume; and that such protection is not afforded by existing legislation, under which the government may take no action until after the food has been placed upon the market and injury may have occurred. Your Committee recommends, therefore, that the Federal Food, Drug, and Cosmetic Act be amended to require that chemicals employed in or on foods be subjected to substantially the same safety requirements as now exist for new drugs and meat products. Adequate provisions for a comprehensive judicial review of administrative decisions should be included in such an amendment.

In view of the immense amount of testimony and the expenditure of time, money, and effort in reviewing the problem, subsequent developments are meager indeed. In 1954 the Hale Amendment to the Food and Drug Law was passed to speed up issuances of food standards. This has brought little concrete results as there are still more nonstandard than standard foods.

On July 22, 1955 a weak and diluted version of the Committee's recommendations in reference to pesticide legislation was passed, now known as "The Miller Pesticide Chemicals Amendment to the Food and Drug Law." This requires manufacturers to convince the Department of Agriculture that his pesticide is useful in safeguarding specific crops and to submit tests to permit estimating the safety of residues. The FDA may then either exempt the pesticide from control or may prescribe "tolerance levels" to prevent excess residue from reaching consumers.

Buried in the Committee's report is this interesting paragraph, pointing to the fact that all necessary legislation is already in the statutes:

Section 401 of the Federal Food, Drug, and Cosmetic Act authorizes the Federal Security Administrator to define and standardize foods for the purpose of promoting honesty and fair dealing in the interest of consumers. This empowers him to determine whether a chemical proposed for use in a standardized food has been demonstrated to be safe.

CHAPTER XV

Re-establishing the Work

THE TESTIMONY in the hearings of 1950 and 1951 elicited just about every intrinsic fact about current food processing and distribution. Throughout that testimony there was a familiar repetition of the same refrain; there were the same arguments and counterarguments heard in Dr. Wiley's day. The question of what was harmful or harmless in an additive appeared just as debatable as ever. The processors and their chemists were just as busy in creating new substances and processes and putting them into use without necessary guarantees that they were beneficial or improvements over older methods. Their policy was devise, use, and advertise boldly—at the risk of the public.

The same startling differences of opinion Dr. Wiley had encountered among experts were again glaringly evident, particularly in the matter of bread softeners. On the one hand, experiments had shown serious consequences to test animals; on the other hand, no pathology was discovered with alleged application of the very same substances. The difference in results could not have been more conflicting.

Surely the ghost of Dr. Wiley must have hovered over the colloquy between Congressman Horan and Dr. Cameron when persistent questioning finally elicited the fact that no final authority existed to determine the chemical safety of any food additive, that agreement was reached by some vague and undetermined process of balancing opinions among authorities. How empty it all sounded when almost

147

THE BIRTHDAY SEAL

Courtesy of Ass'n of Food and Drug Officials of the U.S.

The official birthday seal which was adopted by the Association of Food and Drug Officials of the United States, to commemorate the fiftieth anniversary of the enactment of the Pure Food and Drug Act.

half a century before a man had supplied the answers to all the riddles being propounded again; a man so able, so uncompromisingly honest, so devoted to his duty that he had set up a practically infallible system of judging foods and enforcing the law.

In other words, all that is necessary is to re-establish the work and principles of Dr. Wiley; to re-create the Bureau of Chemistry as it was when he was in supreme command and make of it again the final and absolute authority on food testing—independent of any consideration but the public welfare, unconcerned with questions of expediency, profit, or catering to favored interests.

What we saw in the intervening years since Dr. Wiley left government service was capture of the Food and Drug Administration by the very same interests he had opposed so diligently. In fighting Dr. Wiley, the technique of subverting the Pure Food Law was developed to a fine art. Through all the years—with all the purported reforms, the hearings and investigations—a fine Italian hand had operated behind the scenes. No matter what legislation was passed, the one stipulation to make the food law effective and practical—placing the burden of proof upon the innovator of a new process or chemical—was studiously avoided.

As matters now stand, a new additive can be used until new and more delicate methods of testing, or new discoveries in science—as in the case of agene and mineral oil—produce conclusive evidence of harm. The product then is withdrawn and replaced by another in which the same doubts and uncertainties might still apply. Without evidence to prove harm, its use is permissible. The incompleteness of scientific knowledge is a factor working for the benefit of processors whereas Dr. Wiley's principles were exactly opposite. The slightest doubt about a substance's toxicity should rule it out. As Dr. Enders had stated in his testimony concerning stilbestrol:

> The history of medicine contains innumerable examples of health hazards that were not recognized at first but which after having been recognized are held responsible for obscure ills that baffled physicians. Physicians are on the whole unaware of the use of diethylstilbestrol in poultry. When this knowledge becomes widespread it is to be expected that reports of the effects of eating diethylstilbestrol in chicken will be associated with some conditions which now pass, not unrecognized but not understood.

We, the people, must face the fact that another Dr. Wiley would be impossible in Washington; he could not be appointed because the FDA has succumbed to Big Business. The many sincere and capable workers in the government service are helpless against the machinations of powerful interests that have clever lobbyists and lawyers working in their behalf. Through the blandishments of advertising they cajole the public into believing their propaganda; they subsidize so-called nutritional experts and dietitians to peddle their products; they establish their own research organizations and chemical studies to insure securing favorable data; they are able to influence the recommendations of purportedly impartial bodies such as the National Research Council and the American Medical Association.

One thing, however, is impossible—to suppress all independence of thought and judgment and all freedom of choice. Everyone has the power to enforce his principles by intelligent food buying and selection. The Hearings revealed some scientists who were dedicated to the highest principles of their professions and capable of leadership in a movement for wholesome foods.

There are also a number of firms keenly anxious only to provide the most wholesome products. The Beechnut Packing Company has been energetic in contracting for the purchase of crops free of pesticide residue. Campbell's Soups, as Mr. Bromfield testified, supplies to its growers excellent scientific pamphlets and information on quality production without the use of sprays.

The intelligent purchaser today will demand full and complete information on the ingredients of every packaged product he buys. Whenever possible, he will try to avoid buying packaged products when he can purchase them in bulk. However, that is fraught with hazards also as it is impossible to know where a food was grown and how it was handled before it came to market.

The purchaser can also be guided by several elementary yet practical principles. One is never to buy a food that contains elements which are not derived from foods, but are products of synthetic chemistry. Anything colored with aniline dye should be taboo as anilines are coal-tar products and hence nonfood substances.

A perusal of the advertising in food trade journals will disclose an alarming prevalence of firms offering by-products from a primary product not a food. For example, the Allied Chemical and Dye

Corporation markets aniline food colors through a subsidiary. Monsanto Chemicals offers benzoic acid and sodium benzoate as "safe" preservatives for fruit juices, cider, fruit preserves and jellies, fountain sirups, pickles, sugar cane juice, beer, and wine musts; benzoated ice and brine drips for preserving fish. Monsanto also recommended dipping ripe fruit into a sodium benzoate solution and preserving honey, molasses, and pineapple with its products.

Sustane, an antioxidant, is manufactured by Universal Oil Products. The Union Carbide and Chemical produces a polyethylene plastic food wrapper. The Goodyear Rubber Company has perfected a wrapper for preground coffee which will keep it fresh. Shell Chemical also markets an antioxidant under the brand name of "Ionol."

Dow Chemical produces a propylene glycol for bread softening. Span, Tween, and Myrj 45, the bread softeners so extensively discussed in the Hearings, are all products of the chemical laboratory and derived from petroleum. Pfizer Chemical Company's Sorbistat is used to inhibit growth of molds, yeasts, and certain bacteria which cause spoilage in cheese products, pickles, fish, soft drinks, prepared gelatin, fruit salads, chocolate sirup, and cakes.

The Atlas Powder Company, whose bread softener was described in the Hearings, also markets emulsifiers for the candy and soft-drink industry. The Eastman Kodak Company has patented "Tenox," another antioxidant.

Not one of the products mentioned above originates in a food. They are all chemical substances which imitate the action of natural food elements and are intended to replace them. Every one of them offers increased chances for profit to the food processor; not one of them has any proven nutritional value. The test of their nonessential nature is that foods prepared without them are far more palatable than those which include them.

A number of processes have come into acceptance about which little is known. Homogenization for example is one. Little is said about this process, which is an abomination somewhat analogous to the bleaching of flour, as it reduces all milk to one indistinguishable and uniform mass. Milk from different farms can be mixed indiscriminately. Homogenized milk, which has also been "enriched" with vitamins, is a production that can only be compared to maraschino cherries for its compounding of debasement.

The late Sidney W. Dean, an editor and truly great amateur cook, wrote an amusing if somewhat sardonic article, "This Homogenized World," published in *The Atlantic Monthly* for August 1956. He described an incident in which a mother found a cache of cream in a refrigerator and decided to instruct her two daughters in the art of churning butter.

She churned and churned to no avail. Her daughters drifted off, tired of watching her. Exhausted and mystified, the lady finally fished out a discarded cream container and examined it. The cream was homogenized, which meant all the fat globules had been broken down and uniformly dispersed. She could have churned until dooms-day without getting butter. Mr. Dean wrote:

> Homogenization is one of those sharp ideas that cut both ways. It is the sort of idea that the American purveyor, having once glimpsed its possibilities, is never able to get enough of. Having discovered homogenization as a way of making minimum-standard milk seem better than it is, he started applying the process to other commodities with the same hope. . . . Time was when the owner of a good Guernsey or two gloried in cream that could be skimmed off the setting pans in leathery sheets that would not pour and had to be scraped off the skimmer with a knife; at the right temperature, it would be butter in a fraction of a minute. Homogenized it will pour, all right, it will be butter never and there is certainly nothing about it to glory in. Superiority is traded for convenience; and we plume ourselves on convenience as the definition of superiority.

Dean's article is a classic by a man who learned his foods in the unsophisticated horse-and-buggy era. Lard and peanut butter were two other once wonderful foods which he lamented had become homogenized and consequently ruined by reducing quality to a low and uniform standardization, all for the sake of convenience. Flour of distinct quality, once bought by the barrel, is now a uniform, all-purpose affair. This standardization has even spread to the grow-ing of uniform and more conveniently handled crops. For example, yellow corn in place of the far superior white, and fruits which trans-port better but have little flavor. Tomatoes also have been bred for size, appearance, and lack of seeds—at the expense of palatability. Mr. Dean compared the triumphs of plant breeding to "improving the hardness out of a diamond or the humor out of a joke."

Other observers with a memory for the fruits of their boyhood have remarked on the singular deterioration in our various fruits, which some people attribute merely to nostalgia. Apples, watermelons, strawberries, peaches, and pears somehow do not seem to have the flavor and taste one would expect. Possibly it is the effects of plant breeding, plus the continued use of sprays which saturate the soil and then are taken up through the roots of fruit trees and plants with consequent impairment of flavor.

Leonard Wickenden, author of *Our Daily Poison*, remarked about the delicious flavor of apples from an old, untended tree, growing in the woods. He wondered why our commercial apples could not have such delicious qualities. The answer is probably in the conditions of modern agriculture where there is such a greedy insistence that every last apple be gathered and sold. There is some curious idea that unharvested apples are so much waste or loss, when actually they serve a very useful purpose as plant food. The insignificant loss of fruit through codling moths and other age-old insects has never justified the increasing frenzy for spraying. Opponents of the practice say that insects never destroyed more than 10 or 15 per cent of a crop and usually attacked overripe fruit at that. Discarded fruit can nourish the tree and therefore have some value.

In the wilds, very little of a fruit tree's crop would be consumed; most of it would fall to the ground, decay, and serve as plant food for the next year. Consequently all the sugar, starch, and other components of the fruit would be taken up again through the roots. In this way each year's crop would become sweeter and sweeter. Commercial fruit growers who try to harvest every last ounce of a crop are thereby robbing their trees of food. As Dr. Albrecht testified, the question of the proper compost for a soil is very important. "Pine needles are the best food for pine trees." Would it not be just as true that apples are the best food for apple trees, and if a fair portion of each year's crop were allowed to rot on the ground it would be of benefit to the quality of the next year's crop and the production of better and better apples?

Another in the list of modern abominations — in addition to homogenization, spraying, and fruit and vegetable breeding for more commercially suitable crops—is water fluoridation. This is another instance of the promotion of a nonnutritive substance in our foods, as technically water is a food and comes under the provisions of the Pure Food Act.

To sum up fluoridation briefly, waste products of aluminum manufacture and the fertilizer industry were a huge disposal problem. Some years back it was observed that in areas with a high fluoride content in the water supply the incidence of tooth decay was low. Other observers have pointed out, however, that in some of these areas there was also a great prevalence of other diseases of the teeth, and that the water also contained other elements, besides fluorine, which may have been responsible for decreased tooth decay.

At any rate, people with aluminum residues to sell hit upon the idea of adding it to water supplies at a good price. A campaign of ballyhoo, of misrepresentation, of coercion, and hysteria was begun that for sheer effrontery was a classic. The U.S. Public Health Service became the agency for the promotion of fluoridation at public expense. Officials traveled all over the country enlisting the support of PTA organizations, paid propagandists were hired at fancy fees, movies were shown, and expensive brochures were published. Every means of influencing public opinion was brought to bear in favor of fluoridation.

Opponents were labeled as crackpots. The American Dental Association also became an advertising agency for fluoridation and was ready to invoke its infamous "Article 20" by professionally ostracizing any dentist who dared to oppose the official endorsement. The American Medical Association, through the *pronunciamentos* of Dr. Lull, general manager, also is represented as favoring the measure.

Fluoridation was initially proposed as a ten-year experiment in which results at Grand Rapids, Michigan and Newburgh, New York were to determine its value. Long before the ten-year period was over, fluoridation had been installed in many communities because, as the promoters said with a perfectly straight face, "the public demanded it." They did not mention how they had "played the piano" on public opinion to arouse that demand.

Naturally, the fluoridation promoters did not have too much to worry about in being assured of proper data to substantiate their claims as to the value of fluoridation. The usual favorable results were compiled. These statistics of inhibited tooth decay through the use of fluoridation have been criticized and analyzed as thoroughly misleading and inaccurate by opponents of the measure. Here again are the typical conflicting opinions of experts, as contrasting as the results of the experimental ingestion of bread softeners.

Another danger to public health is in the poultry industry. In recent years it too has become Big Business but regulation of it has not kept pace with production. *Red Book* magazine for August 1956 contained a startling article—"How Safe Is the Poultry You Eat?"—which is enough to raise one's hair. In this article, Dr. Oscar Sussman, chief veterinarian of the New Jersey State Department of Health is quoted:

> In far too many plants sick poultry and well poultry are handled by the same employees, scalded in the same pots, cut open on the same tables and chilled in the same vats, so that even though only one chicken in a hundred is infected to begin with, the whole hundred may be shipped to market carrying any one of some 26 diseases which are shared by man and bird.

That the FDA is cognizant of the dangers in poultry processing, was acknowledged by George T. Daughters, Chief of the Chicago District, in a speech at Ann Arbor, Michigan on September 8, 1956:

> Recently there has been a tremendous amount of publicity on the use of dressed poultry. USPHS studies show that poultry and poultry dishes are responsible for one out of every four cases of food bourne poisoning. The Congress has indicated intense interest in the poultry field and it may be that some compulsory inspection will be instituted in the not too distant future."

When it is remembered that much of this poultry is now being produced by the artificial stimulation of stilbestrol to begin with, the final value of the product cannot be much over zero. The poultry industry, as the authors of the aforementioned article point out, also reflects the vast changes in our living that have come about. Once the housewife could buy live poultry, inspect it for evidence of disease, and clean it carefully herself after slaughter. Any trace of disease in the entrails was quickly brought to the attention of the butcher and no words were minced.

Today we have the era of hastily and quickly prepared meals. Often both husband and wife work and come home at the same time. There is a tendency to eat quickly-prepared foods and little chance to learn the genuine art of cookery which takes time, patience, and effort. These changes in our living have placed us at the mercy of food processors and purveyors, for human nature is human nature. If there is no check on what they are doing, no demand for high quality, and a tendency to accept everything that is cleverly advertised they can do just as they please—and it pleases them to strive for profits at the cost of quality.

Possibly the most hopeful sign of the times is the growing co-operative movement in which consumers are organizing among themselves to form industries and enterprises operated for their mutual benefit. If a canning factory, a poultry packer, a bakery, meat packer, or distributing agency were owned and operated by consumers for the welfare of consumers, there would be a much better chance to procure all that is good and wholesome and at a possible saving.

The Cooperative League has been doing commendable work in one very necessary direction—emphasizing the importance and value of truthful labeling. The co-op label has been permitted on only those products made in the consumer's interest which meet U.S. government standards. Some co-ops also maintain their own testing kitchens, not only to check on the quality of merchandise made by associated co-operatives but other products as well. This careful watchdogging must inevitably be of advantage to the consumer.

The co-operatives have been striving for a better Food and Drug Act—one that would place the burden of proof upon the processor and require him first to secure a certificate of approval for his food ingredients or processes, as is already in effect on drugs. They maintain a Washington bureau and constantly watch legislation on behalf of the consumer's interest. They have sought stronger enforcement of Federal Trade Commission regulations in application to food advertising practices.

An example of how the FDA can oppose the aims of better nutrition is its opposition to Triple Rich bread, from the formula of Dr. Clive McCay. The co-operatives, led by a group in Ithaca, had enthusiastically adopted the bread, which evidently aroused the alarm of the big millers.

While Triple Rich bread was increasing in demand, both among co-op buyers and among commercial bakers using the Triple Rich label and formula, the FDA proposed new bread standards for white and enriched bread. They froze the wheat germ content at 1½ per cent, food yeast at 3 per cent, and soy flour at 3 per cent. Milk solids in commercial breads usually amount to about 3 per cent.

On the other hand, the co-ops insisted on open formula labeling. Their Triple Rich was certified to contain 2 per cent wheat germ, 6 per cent high protein soy flour, and 8 per cent milk solids—without chemicals of any kind. Clearly this was a much better bread than the FDA was proposing as standard. Plainly, Triple Rich was too good, illustrating the possibility that foods above the low level of standardization requirements are kept off the market by prosecuting the processors for violating the Pure Food Law. All this confirms Dr. Wiley's protest in his *History of a Crime* that the Pure Food and Drug Act was perverted to protect adulteration and debasement rather than enforced to protect the health of the public.

Jerry Voorhis, secretary of the Cooperative League—in protesting the FDA-proposed standards in the Hearings—pointed to the higher milk content in Triple Rich, which the Department of Agriculture considered determined the quality of a bread. He said the public was being cheated when bakers failed to state that content on their bread label, because:

> When the consumer is prevented from buying as white bread a product that does tell him how much milk solids and other nutritious ingredients it contains, I submit that the law is being perversely utilized not to protect the consumer but to his detriment.

As of this writing, nothing has materially changed in the status of Triple Rich bread. A phone call to the Chicago office of the FDA brought the information that opposition to Triple Rich was not based on its classification as a white bread, but to its enrichment above food standards. The informant mentioned that it was just as much a violation to exceed standards as to fail to meet them and cited a suit brought against Quaker Oats because one of its products had greatly exceeded enrichment standards.

How the standardization of our foods work to lower their general quality can be appreciated from the disheartening experience of the Buitoni Foods Company. This firm attempted to market a macaroni with a 20 per cent protein content whereas the standard had been set at 13 per cent by weight. After long and expensive litigation which the Buitoni Company had to fight at its own expense, the courts decided that a food which failed to conform to the standard (in this case a food that exceeded required values) was misbranded, even though the deviation was correctly labeled.

Here again is a case of perverting the intent of the pure food law which Dr. Wiley protested so vigorously in his *History of a Crime.* Surely, the purpose of setting a standard was to prescribe the minimum requirements and therefore protect the public from inferior products. When a processor is inspired to produce a food quality far beyond the minimum requirements, surely the law was not meant to harass and restrict him as if he were guilty of a violation. Yet that is exactly how the law was interpreted in the Buitoni case. The court based its decision on a trial decided against a manufacturer who had attempted to market a catsup preserved with benzoate of soda. His label, "catsup with preservative," though accurate, was deemed a violation of the standard as it no doubt was. Just why this also applied to a food processor who felt the public would like a product of higher quality, made of raw materials better than usual and dietetically superior, is somewhat baffling. Through such decisions superior quality is shut off, to the loss of the public and the profit of those who cannot compete with quality.

One of the arguments used by vested interests, to ridicule the contention that chemical additives are dangerous and causative factors in many diseases, is to point to the steadily lengthening life span. People are healthier than ever, they contend. There is more cancer, heart disease, and other afflictions because people are living to an age when they become subject to such ailments.

This is of course a facile and clever argument which has its flaws. The increasing life span can also be attributed to better public health measures which have purified our waters, eliminated bad living and working conditions, and brought cures for many diseases which were formerly fatal. Changing conditions have brought an enormous change in the type of maladies that a doctor must treat.

On this point, the English nutritional authority, Dr. Franklin Bicknell, wrote penetratingly in his interesting little volume, *The English Complaint.* Dr. Bicknell discloses that an alarming tendency toward fatigue, irritability, and work weariness has been noted in the English population since the end of World War II. He attributes this tendency to the steadily decreasing quality of their foods, which is even lower than ours as England is dependent so greatly on food imports. In commenting on increasing longevity, Dr. Bicknell writes:

The grim fact is that we have changed frank illnesses for the insidious dry rot of the degenerative illnesses and endless trivial maladies.

It is very possible that modern conditions which require so little physical effort because of mechanization enable people to exist much longer. Many people would die sooner if they lived under the old primitive conditions in which only the strong and healthy could survive. These factors must also be taken into account.

Regardless of the tendency of processors to disclaim any connection between the use of chemical additives and the rise in cancer and other malignant diseases, concern is growing. In August 1956 cancer specialists from all over the world gathered in Rome and voted unanimously to recommend precautionary action against the use of suspicious additives. Specifically they recommended:

Only authorized additives to food and drink.

A list of authorized substances with constant and instant revision in the light of new data.

Additives should conform to agreed specifications, be of proven harmlessness, a recognized need, and be in the interest of the consumer.

Amounts should be minimal and the consumer should not be misled as to the quality of the food.

Precautions were also recommended against unintentional additives, such as spray residues, etc.

Dr. W. C. Hueper, environmental cancer chief of the National Institute of Health, cautioned against the stilbene family of synthetic food dyes which has been recently introduced as coloring matter in household detergents for cleaning kitchen utensils, dishes, and cooking equipment. Carcinogenic contaminants can also come in foods from water or soils polluted with known carcinogens such as radioactive matter, arsenicals, selenium, and polycyclic hydrocarbons contained in ship fuel oils.

Heat also can transform noncarcinogenic foods into carcinogenic ones and in this category Dr. Hueper mentioned excessively toasted bread or biscuits and excessively grilled or roasted meats, and hydrocarbon constituents of mineral oils freed by cracking of the oil when used as a fat substitute and subjected to heat in packing. New car-

cinogenic compounds in foods can also be formed during processing
—from interaction with other constituents or processing procedures. Plastics used as wrapping material, sausage skins, and coating
material of fruits, cheese, meat, butter, and can linings also carry
similar hazards.

Radiating energy must also be highly suspect, according to Dr.
Hueper. This is extremely interesting because the army is conduct-
ing extensive investigations on sterilizing food by radiation, although
Dr. Hueper states:

> No reliable information exists and no adequate experi-
> mental studies have been made for establishing the noncar-
> cinogenic nature of the radiation products, although both
> types of radiation (ultraviolet and ionizing) are eminently
> carcinogenic when acting on living tissues of both man and
> various species of animals.

Obviously the new food technology is increasing the hazards of
living. The constantly growing list of new chemicals and processes
being used has not only a cumulative effect from continued ingestion,
but an increasingly combined effect. The addition of various chemicals can alter the effects of other chemicals considered relatively
harmless. The new discoveries of danger in substances once considered safe may be due to new combinations with other chemicals.
The addition of fluorides to water, for example, may result in increasing the potential harm in sodium benzoate or some other legally
permissible additive. The possibilities are endless.

In conclusion, to reap the rewards of Dr. Wiley's legacy, we must
re-establish the work of his life by insisting on pure and safe foods
—as fresh as possible, as close to their original state as possible, and
grown on healthy soils and in accordance with scientific agricultural
practices. They must be foods of known quality and digestibility
—appetizing, pleasing, and fragrant. And as the years pass, this
knowledge of proper food selection is becoming increasingly vital
not only to maintenance of health and vigor but to survival. The
benefits of wholesome foods are a matter of individual responsibility
and effort rather than dependence upon legislation or government
administration.

THE END

BIBLIOGRAPHY OF DOCTOR WILEY'S
PUBLISHED BOOKS

Principles and Practice of Agricultural Analysis: A manual for the estimation of soils, fertilizers, and agricultural products. For the use of analysts, teachers, and students of agricultural chemistry. Easton, Pa.: Chemical Publishing Co., 1894-1897. 3 Vols. Second Edition, 1906-1908; Third Edition, 1926-1931.

Foods and Their Adulteration: Origin, manufacture, and composition of food products; description of common adulterations, food standards and national food laws and regulations. Philadelphia: Blakiston Co., First Edition, 1907; Second Edition, 1911; Third Edition, 1917.

1001 Tests of Foods, Beverages and Toilet Accessories. Arranged by A. L. Pierce. New York: Hearst's International Library Co., 1914.

Not By Bread Alone, The Principles of Human Nutrition. New York: Hearst's International Library Co., 1915.

The Lure of the Land: Farming after Fifty. New York: The Century Co., 1915.

Beverages and Their Adulteration, Origin, composition, manufacture, natural, artificial, fermented, distilled, alkaloidal and fruit juices. Philadelphia: Blakiston Co., 1919.

The History of a Crime Against the Food Law, The amazing story of the national food and drugs law intended to protect the health of the people, perverted to protect adulteration of foods and drugs. Washington, D.C.: H. W. Wiley, 1929. Reproduced by photolithography, Milwaukee, Lee Foundation for Nutritional Research, 1955.

Harvey W. Wiley, An Autobiography. Indianapolis: Bobbs-Merrill, 1930.

𝒥NDEX

162

Peas, 35, 86
Pesticides, 7, 126, 140, 141, 145, 146
Phosphoric acid, 144
P-4000, 121
Pineapples, 89
Plums, 45
Poison Squad, 40, 41, 43, 49, 50
Pork cuts, 68
Potash, 79
Potatoes, 84, 85
Poultry, 68, 71, 136-137, 155
Preservatives, chemical, 35, 41, 45, 65,
    75, 106; *also see* Poison Squad
Preserves, fruit, 90, 91
Protein, of cell, 6
Pumpernickel, 80
Purdue University, 22, 23
Pure Food Law, 33-46
    amendments, 110, 123, 146
    commemorative stamp, 9
    passes Congress, 46
    perversion of, 47, 54, 149, 157, 158

R

Radiated foods, 160
Ray, F. E., 113
Refrigeration, 63
Remsen Board, 49, 50, 118
Rice, 80
Roosevelt, Theodore, 31, 48-49
Rye flour, 80, 81

S

Saccharin, 48, 49, 55, 79, 80, 86, 90
Salad oils, 93
Salicylates, 35, 42, 45, 50, 90, 91, 127
Salt
    preservative, 39, 69, 76
    substitutes, 123, 129
Saltpeter, 35, 65, 67
Sardines, 36, 72
Sausages, 35, 36, 67
Scheele, L. A., 113, 140
Selenium, 140
Shellfish, 73
Shortening, 92
Shrimp, 73
Sirups, 35, 97, 98
Soft drinks, 102
    cola, 103, 143, 144
    flavors, 103
    industry, 116
Sorghum, 15, 23
    research, 27, 28
Soybeans, 138
Spaghetti, 83, 84
Spices, 86
Stabilizers, 117

Standards, food, 126, 128
Starch, 67
Stearin, 36, 67, 91, 94
Stilbestrol, 130, 136-137, 149, 155
Subtilin, 118, 119
Sugar, 95
    adulteration, 98
    beet, 29, 94, 95
    bleaching, 97, 98
    cane, 29, 95, 96, 97
    canning with, 79
    dextrose, 87
    economics of, 95
    fruit, 87
    granulated, 96
    levulose, 87
    maple, 96, 97
    research, 25, 29-31
    in soft drinks, 102
    sorghum, 15, 23, 27, 28
Sulfite, 79
Sulfur dioxide, 37, 39, 48, 79, 88, 96,
    97, 104, 106, 115, 118, 121
Sulfurous acid, 35, 55, 83, 89
Sulphate, 35
    copper, 55, 86
Sunflower oil, 93
Sweeteners, artificial, 116;
    see also Saccharin

T

Taft, President, 50
Tannin, 87
Tapioca, 86
Tartaric acid, 87, 89
Tea, 104
Theobromin, 102, 103, 105
Thiourea, 116, 125, 145
Tomatoes, 86, 127, 152
Triple Rich bread, 144, 156-157
Truffles, 94
Turmeric, 86

U

Ultramarine blue, 97
Umber, 36

V

Veal, cuts, 66
Vegetables, 84
    adulteration, 86
    canning, 85
    dehydrated, 115
    oils, 67, 91
Vinegar, 35, 36, 65
Vitamin
    A, 118, 124

Collier's for January 13 1906

THE GREAT AMERICAN FRAUD

By SAMUEL HOPKINS ADAMS

V—PREYING ON THE INCURABLES

Collier's for April 28 1906

THE GREAT AMERICAN FRAUD

"WARRANTED HARMLESS"

VERDICT OF DEATH FROM BULL'S COUGH SYRUP

CANCER IS CURABLE

A Quarter of a Century's Marvelous Success

RHEUMATISM

EPILEPTIC FITS CURED

CANCER CURED

Fits Cured.

DEAFNESS CURED

CONSUMPTION CATARRH CURED—FREE

FITS CURED

Illustration Courtesy Abbott Laboratories, North Chicago, Ill.